RIVER CROSSINGS:
VOICES OF THE DIASPORA

RIVER CROSSINGS: VOICES OF THE DIASPORA

AN ANTHOLOGY ON THE INTERNATIONAL
BLACK EXPERIENCE

Edited by
C. JEROME WOODS

INTERNATIONAL BLACK WRITERS & ARTISTS—LOS ANGELES
LOS ANGELES, CALIFORNIA

Published by International Black Writers & Artists—Los Angeles
First edition, first printing: Summer 1994

International Black Writers & Artists is devoted to providing support, education
and resources to writers and artists, whether aspiring, neophyte, or professional.
Address all correspondence to: International Black Writers & Artists—Los
Angeles: P.O.Box 43576, Los Angeles, California 90043, Voice mail (213)
964-3721.

ISBN: 0-9640477-0-5
Library of Congress Catalog Card Number 94-77063

for the ancestors,
who founded universities and wrote long before the Mayflower

for the mentors,
the shamen, griots, preachers, teachers, rappers

for our founder,
Mrs. Crutchfield, whose vision and faith guided us thus far

for our past president,
Mark Tanks whose leadership, courage and humility inspired us all

for our seed,
whose generations will make history, recount it and document it

Contents

vii

Preface

The International Black Writers & Artists, Inc. (IBWA) is like my eleventh child; God gave me the strength, wisdom, and stamina to give birth to it after two tragic deaths in my family. In August of 1974 my youngest son, just sixteen and about to attend UCLA, was shot and killed by the Crips. On December 1, 1974 my 89 year-old father was killed by a hit-and-run driver. So IBWA was born out of sadness, depression, and a need to do something for others.

I owe the starting of IBWA to my adopted daughter (our family was always adopting someone), Nina James, whom I affectionately called Gwena. Gwena literally dragged me from workshop to workshop seeking outlets for our writing. We spent a lot of money on workshops, conferences and seminars only to discover that the issues of the Black writer were not being addressed.

In December of 1974, in the midst of my deep depression, and with Nina's insistence, we started Local 1 in Los Angeles with just four people: Nina, Ama Jordan, my oldest daughter Carol Crutchfield, who remains active with local 1, and myself. We met religiously for a year, once a month.

The local grew fast in 1975. Later in the year, we took our famous pot luck down to San Diego in a caravan and Local 2 was born. Next Local 3 was formed in Chicago, followed quickly by Local 4 in New York.

About this time I moved to Oakland and started Local 5. A young poet from San Francisco, Darlene Roberts, attended our meeting and before she could say Jack Robinson, she was President for the new Local 6. One of our Local 5 members moved to Sacramento and requested that we allow her to start Local 7.

Today there are 31 locals, most very active, and five new ones on the horizon. We have expanded across the United States and to the Virgin Islands. I have also had requests to start locals in Dallas, Texas, London, England, and Africa.

IBWA's past is full of people who have become successful,

improved their writing, published their work, had their work become a movie, or attained their goals. This list includes Ted E'bon, Donald Bakeer, Fannie Tatum Hawkins, Gene Williams, Ama Jordan, Adrienne Russell, Edwina Gaines, Winston Moss, Mark D. Tanks, and Regina Chaney to name just a few. We are proud that we have touched so many lives in a positive and rewarding way.

God has blessed me with dedicated IBWA members who have stayed with me through the 20 years. I would especially like to acknowledge those members who have passed on but whose spirits still live through IBWA: Charles McGill, Milton Sallee, William Prince, Hilton Jordan, Ted E'bon, Josephine Alexander and Arnold Chevalier, whose death was tragic and untimely. I will dedicate our Black Book Club to this outstanding young man. When we are able to get our IBWA center I will name a room after each of these devoted members. Our goal is to establish an IBWA Cultural Center, which will house the IBWA Credit Union, a gallery, a theater and meeting rooms.

I am extremely proud of Local 1, the Los Angeles chapter. They execute and host the Annual July Workshop/Conference, which requires hard work and extensive planning.

I also want to thank members of the Los Angeles chapter who served on the Anthology Committee; their tireless effort and perseverance have made this book a reality—something that succeeding generations can see, read and know that we left a legacy for them to follow in our footsteps. We have had two other anthologies, *The Black View of the Bicentennial* (1976), and *76th and San Pedro* (1986)—which was the address of one of our benefactors, Edwina Gaines, where we met for years. We were made famous at that address by Local 1's Annual pre-Thanksgiving dinners, for which I cooked 30-40 pounds of oxtails and a smoked turkey.

As you can see, IBWA's future looks bright. I would like to see Blacks all over the United States support and celebrate our 20th year conference with us. We are exhilarated to have reached this milestone and hope you come with us into the 21st century.

We hope you enjoy the 20th Anniversary anthology as much as we enjoyed preparing it for you. If you submitted your work to the anthology, our heartfelt thanks. See that as many people as possible read the anthology. Spread the word and above all continue to write.

I will be 77 this year; I appreciate more the things I can see, feel, and hear—like the breezes blowing, the birds singing, the trees turning. Although I can't see well, I am keeping my eyes on the prize.

EDNA CRUTCHFIELD
NATIONAL PRESIDENT AND FOUNDER

Acknowledgments

River Crossings: Voices of the Diaspora* is a life song. Voices are bitter-sweet; memories and journeys short-long. It is a song that required insight and collaboration. It is a song made up of different colors, rhythms, skills, perspectives, lifestyles, beliefs, experiences—lives via Africa. I am grateful for the stronger voices that will leave a legacy and for the weaker ones who will receive and continue it. Without them both, the song of life would be incomplete.

I wish to thank the anthology committee members: Hazel Clayton Harrison, Linda A. Hughes, Larry Newson, and Randy Ross who perpetuated the book's existence. In particular, I am indebted to the contributors who provided body and substance with their submissions to give the anthology breath.

A special thanks to the Review and Selection committee members: Wanda Coleman, Meryl Ginsberg, and David Ulin whose fair and critical eyes helped decide works to be printed. Also, to Ken Wibecan whose copy editing was invaluable, Terry Wilson for designing a great book cover, and Jo-Ann Green-Steward whose cover art exemplified our vision.

In addition, I wish to thank Octavia Butler, Angela Kinamore, Otis O'Solomon and Dr. Leonard Simon for endorsing our endeavors.

Much recognition and appreciation goes to the following individuals, groups, and organizations who performed, attended events, helped raise funds; lent their expertise, office personnel and contributed in many other ways.

ADWÍN	SUNJI ALI	TIM AHSKAR
ERIN AUBRY	RINALDO BARROS	GIL BAYLOR
ALAN BELL	CLYDE BENNETT	CHRISTOPHER BOYD
JANET BROOKS	MICHAEL BROOKS	GENE BROWN
PATRICIA BROWN	RON BROWN	ERNESTO CHARLES
ANNA BELLE COOPER	MARCUS CRISP	MARIA CRISTERNA
JAY DAVIS	RICHARD DEDEAUX	ALTEMAR DIAS
RON DIXON	RITA DYSON	DAVE FERTIG
DAVID FLOT	WAYNE FRENCH	MARGIE GHIZ

HARRY GIPSON   RALPH GLENMORE   ELIMU GOSS
MARK HAILE   AMDE HAMILTON   DARLINE HARRIS
MARY HAWKINS   LEONARD HOWZE   ZERLINE HUGHES
TOYOMI IGUS   KATRICE JACKSON   SHAZZAR KALLIE
SAMMY KAMAU   LANA LOCKE   KENY LONG
MR. MACLIN   GREGORY JEROME MAY   NAFIS NABAWI
DAVID NETTER   LARRY NEWSON   OTIS O'SOLOMON
JUANITA PAREDES   MICHAEL PARSEE   DALE LYA PIERSON
DENISE PINES   JANICE PORTER-MOFFITT   SHARI RANDOLPH
ROBERT RANKIN   JUANA ROSS   RANDY ROSS
KHALID SALAAM   SIDNEY SINGLETON   ETHRIDGE SMITH
ROBERT G. SMITH   KYNARD SPENCER   CARLOS SPIVEY
ROSE STEVENS   BARRY STINSON   LEROY STONEHAM
TAMU   DOROTHY TAYLOR   SHARON TERRY
ANGELA VAUGHN   EUGENE RICHARD VAUGHN   VALLERIE WAGNER
RALPH WALKER   VIRGIE WALKER   JIMI WALTON
PHILL WILSON   MARSHA WIEDERHORN   KEHINDE WILEY
JIMI WALTON   JEANETTE WILLIAMS-SIMMONS   BILLIE WOODS
                        ELOUISE WOODS
                    THE WATTS PROPHETS
                PEOPLE COORDINATED SERVICES
             F.A.M.E. CHURCH DRAMA DEPARTMENT
                    AIDS PREVENTION TEAM
            BLACK GAY & LESBIAN LEADERSHIP FORUM
       CHRIST THE GOOD SHEPHERD EPISCOPAL CHURCH
             HOLMAN UNITED METHODIST CHURCH
                      ST. ELMO VILLAGE
                      UNITY IN SOUNDS
                       RUE'S HOUSE
                    THE CARL BEAN CENTER
                    WIDNEY HIGH SCHOOL
                           BLK
    THE BLACK & LATINO MULTICULTURAL BOOK CENTER/PASADENA
        A DIFFERENT LIGHT BOOKSTORE/HOLLYWOOD
        MIDNIGHT SPECIAL BOOKSTORE/SANTA MONICA

It is with sincere gratitude, humility and reverence that I say
thank you all for sustaining me unconditionally in my "river crossings."

                                              C. JEROME WOODS
                                              EDITOR

Introduction

I have heard the founder of International Black Writers and Artists, Mrs. Edna Crutchfield, say many times that "Writers write!" I know it's not original, but it's clear, eloquent in its simplicity, and its meaning has not been lost on us, her literary and artistic children.

This anthology features the literary efforts of people of color who are following that edict and paying their dues to become the next wave of Toni Morrisons, James Baldwins, Terry McMillans, Dunbars, and Hughes'. The imaginative works culled from the "river crossings" of those lives are laid bare for your enjoyment.

Some will make you laugh, cry, cringe, exult, or more importantly, make you think. I am a firm believer that words in the hands of people who want to use them are more powerful than any atom bomb. Ideas, poems, stories and art put to paper have shaken whole civilizations. I leave it to you to decide if the selections in this volume measure up.

Please allow me to be selfish for a moment in saying that, in many ways, I feel like this is my baby. Back in late 1992, when I was first given the honor of being the president of International Black Writers and Artists, Los Angeles Chapter, the item at the top of my list of things to do was to produce another IBWA anthology. I had no idea how it would be accomplished, but I knew I was in the company of a rare and talented group of real writers and "wannabees" like myself. I knew if we had the will to do it, the talent was definitely there.

They say that dynamite comes in small packages. The explosion that would bring this dream to fruition came from a hard driving, restless, energetic, frustrated perfectionist spark plug (Is that enough adjectives?) of a man named C. Jerome Woods. Now don't get me wrong, there were many more of our group who spent and gave of themselves to produce this tome. I think you are really in for a treat because of their hard work. I don't mention all of their names because I'm afraid I would leave some very important people out. However, I'm sure all will agree that without the doggedness, stubbornness, and just plain sweat of Mr. Woods, River Crossings would still just be a dream and a line on my "To Do" list. I know he is squirming in that nervous manner of his as he reads this, but to him, and to you, the reader, and to this fine group of writers and artists, and everyone involved in this project, I thank you.

LARRY NEWSON
PRESIDENT, IBWA—LOS ANGELES

RIVER CROSSINGS:
VOICES OF THE DIASPORA

*baby/*TALK

if we treated every child like poetry
the history of ourselves would be read and
not forgotten.

if we saw the poetry in our children
we would understand that they are true
Gifts of Light.

if we created children like the poet
creates poetry it would be a true
act of Love.

If we could only read the poetry in our children's
eyes, we would not go foolishly to parenthood.
We would not admonish them vainly nor abuse their
delicate beginnings.

... but we would speak poems to them, softly
and watch them grow from the essence of our

Words...

The Difficulty of Learning

I walked on rainy nights through shiny streets
Passing well turned hands stretched out for a dime
Hollow eyes wanting one more drink
I saw mystic mummy vampire junkies
Stuff orange marmalade through musty bandages
They were hung-out strung-out
Jamming basketball needles in the sunken arms
Of collapsed junction shooting galleries
I saw blood flowing from dead pig eyes
And I learned

I passed lying images in antique mirrors
Never seeing who was on the other side of America
Slick head dope head
Wet head dick head perm head
Yell   Get down it's the A K spray down   Film at 11
And babies cracked up watching John Barleycorn
Dance at innocent bystander funerals
And I learned

I was here in Lotus Land amazed
Why so many are dead and dying
There must be a reason
There must be a reason
Why only the poor are guilty
And everyone else is right
There must be a reason
I'm still trying to learn something

But I can't figure out
Belfast or Johannesburg
I can't figure out why I bothered to learn. I can't
How to read Write Sex drive Pull my willie
Cook Pay rent or flush the toilet
Like all the other things I learned
Because they said should

Now they say I should drink poisoned water but
With a rubber biscuit sewn inside
While I run through smog-choked streets coughing
So I can stay healthy so I won't die
But everywhere everyone's trying to kill you

I want to figure out why I'm here waiting
Doing all the things they said I should
When there's no point
So I keep doing what I can to get through

Miles

Like a question Miles bent over yesterday swinging by a memory
His stretched arms cut pain from hard lips
That pressed music in willowing shades of blue
And played no shame

Returning oceans of sound that never break or
Return through sentimental eyes dramatizing history in a quiet way
Curled hands finger notes
Confiscating violence with darkness
No dancing or singing while high stepping
Like rag tag bar walking niggers
Smiling circus madness shaded green and black

Calloused lip pouting on pungent notes
To stop sanguine floes from rushing
Near urges that occur on cool faces
Entering in books of time
He played sad Spanish blues and tasty valentines without regret
Mashed music under high shoes dipped in dark dream
In rounded midnight corners rolling
Cracked voice Prince of Darkness played black music rocking on
Somehow able to stand on feet sunk in creeping anxiety

Laid out as always cool
Laid out still
His eyes finally closed
The bright light stayed windowed in silent light cathedral
Plays no more
Sh...Peaceful

Jazz

(For the magnificent and charming Rose Gales,
for all the pretty flowers and gentle Roses)

Something mellow, moist
Out of past sentiments
refined,
Magic marbled moments of
Celestial harmony
Dayspringing softness
In a morning flow
A tender piece of slow motion
     rising to a peak of
Unspeakable tenor madness
A piece of yesterday singing
     today
Something warm, poetry
     winging it
Speaking softly of honey
     Waiting for a day train
An evening flower to come and call

Jazz, yesterday you came, midnighting
     like a shooting star that
Fell over Alabama
You were there like a windjammer
A Freddie Freeloader flying high
A friendly fox telling everybody she knows
That Cannonball not only wrote,
     "A Sack O' Woe"

But fathered many sounds that now
     abound in space

And in the hearts of all young lovers
Forever and a day
Jazz, gently you came; you were the
     night rhythm, the down stroke

That caught John Coltrane by surprise
Brought tender tears of love and joy
To his warm, moist soul eyes
You were the memories that
Monk brought to fruition
The "Black" consciousness that
          will never die
Blue Monk will always live
Like a love spring in a night fall

Jazz, you are the ocean spring
          that makes forever moist
Memorable mornings when I
First heard rhythm walk
Joy talk back to a fountain
          head of spring
Telling water free daybreaks
Again and again of deep rivers
Burning lake and running streams
She had all ready seen
Jazz you are my night breeze
You speak of me through a
Canopy of lush green scenes
Keep singing, "Every Day"
Like you and the blues had a "thing" going on
And I was your horn, your daybreak
Your dream walker, your song
After your lover has gone...

Homeboy

(A Sonnet for South Central ELL LAY)

YOU THINK YOU CAME OUT OF WATTS
103RD STREET RHYTHM BAND, CHARLES WRIGHT
AND BEING A FUNKADELIC FAN,

BUT YOU STRAIGHT OUT OF JEFF AND JORDAN
YOU A COASTER LIKE O.B. JESSIE AND BARRY WHITE,
A "YOUNG HEART" THAT GREW BRAVE AND FOUND THE LIGHT.

YOU THINK YOU WAS A SLAUSON, A GLADIATOR
OR BUSINESSMAN AND YOUR SOUL WAS SO FUNKY
IT HAD TO BE BANNED.

BUT YO' PEOPLE WERE CLAIMING PANTHER, US ORGANIZATION
AND TEMPLE #27. THEY WERE STARTING BEAUTIFUL STYLES
ALL THE WHILE THE STREETS WERE DYING UNDER US AT NIGHT.

YOU THINK YO' FOLKS DIDN'T HEAR WHEN MARTIN DIED
AND EVEN THE PREACHERS YELLED, "FIGHT!"
FOR EVEN HOT BLOOD COOLED IN THE FACE OF ENDLESS BLIGHT.

BUT YOU COME FROM B.S.U. ORGANIZERS AND F.B.I. DESPISERS,
YOU COME FROM WATTS RIOTERS AND CESAR CHAVEZ
        SYMPATHIZERS.
YOU STARTED THE MARCH ON WASHINGTON AND HID THE S.L.A.

YO' PAPA WASN'T NO PIMP, AND YO' MAMA NEVER PANDERED.
YOU COME FROM PEOPLE THAT LOVED PEACE AND HAD MANNERS.
YOU SHOULD BE PROUD YOU'RE FROM SOUTH CENTRAL ELL LAY!

YOU COME FROM THE WATTS PROPHETS AND FATHER AMDE.
YOUR PEOPLE WERE MUSLIMS WITH MALCOLM, ELIJAH AND W.D.
AND, ANOTHER THING IS SURE, CUZZ,
YOU'RE BOTH CRIP AND BLOOD.

It's Our Time; It's About Us!
It's About South Central!

It's not about being a criminal—rather than a general.
And, it ain't all about funerals either.

IT'S ABOUT ORGANIZING and sympathizing
With other groups covering each others troops
And if we've got to swoop? Swoopin'

I'm proud to say I'm from South Central L. A.,
A place where gettin' ahead is mostly mental—
but don't get too calm, son,
You might get confronted by a gun!

It could be march 29th and 3:15
justice and the traffic light on Florence and Normandie
Could have just turned green when the MAU MAU
Finally discover the chemical powers of gasoline.

It's about seeing that comin' and maybe runnin'.
But, if necessary confrontin' but only what is necessary to confront.
In fact, it's better to have prepared for this out front.
It's not about who we fought; It's about training the brunt of this
        juggernaut!

Now, it's about them not getting caught
And incarcerated or economically emasculated.
Their powers must be refined.
We're losing too many strong minds.

We need legitimate business men
From both the upper and lower end of our spectrum.
This protocol between classes that has kicked all of our—
Is simply stupid and dumb!

You 8 Tray Gangster Crips must become
The 83rd Street Youth Association.

A legitimate enterprise that solicits funds
For saving the youth of our nation.

And Rolling Sixties must get busy with the creation
Of the Rolling 60's Street Youth Organization
Before they lose another 'Lil Fee or Stone.
Great brothers can't hide; they must be known.

Now is T-Mac's time and all the Blood Nation
To become the UYBBA, Inc. (United Young Blood Brothers
        Association.)
Loaf and the Lot Boys from Bounty Hunters
Must become Nickerson Garden's Youth Foundation.

Capitalize thru tax exempt donations
From every liberal company and corporation.
Sell a neighborhood business service—24 hour Graffiti Insurance,
A sticker in their window with your logo for visible assurance.

Your councilmen will cooperate.
Tell them you need a storefront, free, to operate.
Solicit money and be frank,
Then send then a letter and your thanks.

The damage is done, now, take the land that you've won.
no more confusion; this is The Revolution.

Superman Visited Me the Other Day

Superman visited me the other day
Wearing a suit and a paisley tie.

He leaped over hurdles that tried to stifle my happiness,
Caught the words in his hands that were shot at my heart,
Blew out the flames that tried to consume my spirit,
Sped past the pain on its way to my brain
And caught it with white cotton teeth
Flew ahead of me to another time and brought me back to
        a life I thought had ended.

Superman visited me the other day and told me I was his
        superwoman.

Now we fly together.

The Fifth Definition

It is a house that you have passed; that one house that you imagine yourself in as you go by on pleasant Sunday afternoons. It is a house that can become your obsession. The memory of that house returns to you and mitigates your urban Wednesdays. Of course, you reason, as you enter the green of the suburbs, no owner would willingly give it up, and how awful it is for you to wish divorce, or something worse, on complete strangers.

It is a big house with a straight, strong facade and large, sublimely long windows that are sheathed by drapery, linings and shades. That's one thing you will—would—do differently. When—if you ever can—you call this place home, you will use all that promised natural light; for what would be the purpose of having so many open-for-inspection windows if you block the view?

Driving on, you have the impression that light never reaches into that house. You wonder aloud, "Who lives there?"

A man, a woman, and their children inhabit the structure.

Who lives there? In winter a cat lounges next to the heater, between coordinated sheers and streak-free windowpanes in summer. On a bedroom night stand, a fish wafts along in his octagonal world, the sixth in a line of ill-fated common *carassius auratus*. Reposing in the insulated attic, a wood rat waits for night. They live.

The man, and the woman, and the children inhabit the house.

The children...

Charles is as sound and as practical as his name. He was born at a time when everything was solid but the present and children of solid futures had to have names built on tradition and potential tax brackets. Names like Charles. It was a name that could be characterless (Charlie) or familiar (Chuck) or pretentious (C.W.—his mother's maiden name, Wallace, was preserved through him); or it could be more substantial just by the inflection and modulation of the voice; Ch arles or Charl... and a long pause that you must hold your breath through, wait for it, not yet, one more second and ...es.

Charles is twelve.

Her mother envisioned country garden and misty moors and wars to be fought over the rose of her daughter when she decided on

Guenever. She could not be swayed from it. If the truth were to be told, the man did not really try to change her mind, he delighted in the pouty stubbornness that made her exhausted face glow and only pretended to detest the name "Guenever" to maintain that moment. The woman would mold her Guenever for some Arthur or Lancelot. Moody, and indomitable, a light-headed eccentricity there. Guenever. Never Gwen or slip-of-the-tongue, Gu'never. Always planned and exact, Guenever.

Guenever will soon be ten.

And Audwith. He was not the last but it is always "and Audwith." Like someone handing you a well thought out shopping list that will take you two hours to properly fill, and as you are pulling out the drive, they yell from the door, "And Audwith!" You don't hear this and would have quickly forgotten it if you had. They will fuss when you return, "You forgot the Audwith," but, "I wouldn't have used it anyway. It would have spoilt in the fridge. Still it would have been nice to have," and "What does one do with Audwith, anyway?"

Becky is the last child. Sunny and bright and wanted, needed for holding and kissing and cooing over. She came as Rebecca and remained as Beck, cuddled in that cold house.

Beck is four.

And Audwith is seven.

They reside in the house you have pictured in your mind when you set aside a little from your paycheck every month. Charles, Guenever, Beck and Audwith, and the man and the woman reside there. That's how the man would put it. Asked, he would grin as if the question were a joke that he knew he could top, "I reside at 20234 West Bent Twig Circle." With So-Comfort, the cat, and Harry, the fish, and the wood rat who nibbles insidiously above their heads.

The man is dominated by the necessity of routine. He did not get where he is by being lazy and wasteful of time. He cannot abide people who do not wear watches that are accurate, and do not carry date books that are neatly worn from use and in easy reach for correlation with the watch. Except for the morning of December 25th (when he may sleep until nine), the man is up at 5:30. He springs from bed. Weighted wrist and ankle bands are wrapped on after the jogging suit is pulled on over the jock strap that was snapped into place. He limbers up as he goes down the stair, using the banister as his barre. He takes one final stretch against the door jamb before he steps out in the cool and damp of early dawn. Up the drive, around the bends of Bent Twig Circle, on to an off-shoot, turning back by the precise maneuvering of cul-de-sacs and walkways, behind the houses and along what was originally meant to be a bridle path but has become a tie-rutted, secluded niche popular with high school students. To the man's horror it is often littered with smashed six-pack cartons, packets of cigarette papers and sodden condoms. He sometimes thinks of moving when he sees these hidden pockets of his neighborhood, but the thoughts are already fleeing as he turns back on to his street and looks at his house. How could any man leave that?

Panting, sweating, dripping odor, he swoops down for the paper and opens his door. In one fluid motion he closed the door, dropped the paper and began to strip. It's 6:11 when he steps into the downstairs shower.

The woman joins him at the closet. And they kiss. A quick tending to her own toilette and "Time for *my* morning jog," she jokes before stopping downstairs. She puts toast on a platter for the microwave. She grinds coffee and begins to whip eggs in a bowl. Eggs in the skillet, the Jen Aire grill is made ready for the children's breakfast. The man comes, holds the unfolded paper across his lap while he butters his toast and eats his eggs. 6:45. The Lexus is out on the street as the garage door bows.

Every Sunday and Wednesday evening the woman prepares a large Tupperware dispenser of pancake batter. Every morning she stirs the cold batter and decides what is special about the day. If it is warm, she goes tropical and mashes bananas into the batter. On a cold morning, she might add applesauce, nutmeg and raisins. Company? Heavy cream for richness, a dash of brandy. Sleepovers? Then it was time for food coloring and strategically placed bits of dried fruit or nuts to form a smiling face as the pastel pancake is turned over on the young guest's place. She has variations on any theme.

At 7:15 Charles descends, school ties, polished shoes, manicured mails, brushed hair, regulation blazer turned inside out and carefully placed on the back of his chair. He kisses her cheek, maintaining the aloofness that she, labeling it strength, admires as her own stitch in his attire.

Promptly late, Guenever floats in carrying ribbons for her braids and her golden box of earrings. She chatters and flutters while her mother ties her braids down and slips her fourteen karat post in.

And Audwith. Later. Shoes untied because he'd been distracted by a shadow a tree cast just as he'd bent to pull the laces. And anyway, he's forgotten socks, or did not have time for them, or could not find two he felt good about (matching did not matter), or he simply did not wear socks and did not tie his shoes because today he simply wanted to feel the frayed tips of his laces hitting his ankles, he would explain when asked. He may frown and mumble, "Hello," if it's demanded. Or, he may beam sunshine into usually gloomy corners and shout his greeting joyously—bright, booming, ready to bounce about the room or leap out a window.

Beck will arrive behind him. In pajamas, she will come as if tethered to him.

She will clutch other security; lately a bear that had been with all her siblings. Only with Audwith, it had lost an eye and needed an ear stitched back on. It is known as That Bear of Audwith's and the man often threatens to toss it away. Beck treats it as one would a wounded hero just returned from unspeakable but justified horrors.

The children eat together. The woman fusses over Charles' tie and Guenever's hair ribbons. "Someone forgot socks," she reprimands. "I have slipper," Beck intones, setting her mother to gushing over her sweetness. "Mama's Fresh Cream," the woman calls her and Audwith's socks are forgotten.

Off to school—Charles with an air of important matters that need his immediate attention, Guenever and Audwith to wait in the drive for the bus. Guenever chirps while swinging her book bag and Audwith pokes about in the bushes and gutter for something to fill his pockets. Beck stands on a stool by the window talking first to That Bear of Audwith's and then to Audwith, who responds to her attention with waves every few seconds.

When Beck informs her that her middle two have boarded the bus, the woman rushes her youngest upstairs, rolls her out of pajamas and folds her into overalls. Hair barrettes are made to clutch tiny, tight curls and ears are inspected. Into the Volvo wagon, past the shopping mall where "Mama's Smart Girl" can read the names of all the department stores, and to the Children's Colony they go, Repeated kisses and reminders and there is always a sigh behind her as she manages the steps alone, "have a happy day, Mama's big Girl."

Back at the house, the woman will straighten; a lady who comes thrice weekly, cleans. The woman will go to the freezer and find whatever she needs to keep up to date with the menu she prepared at the beginning of the month. She will check bedrooms, bathrooms, and cabinets to up-date her shopping list. She will make phone calls and then dress after a long bath. She will go to her meetings, do her shopping, her volunteer work. If it is Wednesday, she will attend a later morning ceramics class; she hopes to make a set of pots for her begonias. Or she will learn how to arrange the flowers she began to grow in her garden after a horticulture class she took at the junior college. She will stay busy until it is time to pick up Beck.

Dinner is steaming on the table when the man arrives home. His children are present with clean hands folded. Heads bow and words are chanted. Dinner is served.

After dinner, Charles never has to be reminded of homework. He has usually completed it, and so he sits at his desk with his slide rule or he works at his computer. He has other projects: a model ship, a doll house for Guenever's birthday, a robot for his brother's. The man helps him occasionally but senses that Charles prefers to work alone and does not impose upon him often.

Guenever and the woman go over factors and decimals in the kitchen. Guenever rattles off related facts, usually lopsided and illogically connected, and then announces the name of her newest best friend. "What happened to..." her mother asks. Guenever tells her of shared secrets too broadly spread about, or jump ropes not being turned in quite the way she had asked.

And Audwith is there, nearby. Having been ignored by Charles long enough, he has stumbled into the kitchen. His math is done properly, or obscured by drawings of aliens or mutants. "Guenever won't jump double dutch."

She is startled to find him in the doorway, "One rope is enough," the woman says after a moment,

"All the girls jump double dutch."

"Not me!"

"My teacher jumps double dutch, Mama." Audwith says, quickly adding, "After school," because he does not think his mother would approve of teachers jumping rope at any other time.

The woman places her tongue on the back of her front, upper teeth and draws in air. "Your teacher lets you draw instead of work." That she, the teacher, leaves a lot to be desired is the unvoiced—but logical—conclusion.

And Audwith wants to counter this, but before he can, Beck enters, making her rounds. A kiss from Mama, a maternal pinch from Guenever, a pat from Charles, and Audwith takes her into a grasping, enveloping bear hug until she squeals. Daddy wants to know why there is so much noise. Baby-scented and moist from her bath, Beck goes to him. Daddy takes her up the stairs. He watches the toothbrushing, gives a story, offers a toy, settles reluctantly on That Bear of Audwith's "for one more night," and shuts her eyes with kisses.

He's in his routine. A game with Charles while the dishes are being done. He plays with Guenever, who delights him with her unadorned charm. He might arm wrestle with Audwith or debate him, or just stare at him awed, wondering from where he might have come. Good nights and more kisses. He fills his pipe and reads whatever periodicals have appeared next to his lounging char. Upstairs, a kiss, a decision. If he decides negatively, he will go back downstairs, lock up and wander the large rooms—wait her out. If he decides affirmatively, he will rush through securing his residence and vaults up the stairs humming.

Sleep. Baby snores and murmurs; Audwith talks in his dreams. Charles may read late. So-Comfort, the car, grooms herself. The fish circles a plastic castle with eyes up to follow the ascent of bubbles. The wood rat rises with a yawn.

5:30 comes again.

Routine. Consistency. Quality time with the children. Occasional sex. His single taste of tobacco. This is the man: set by proven routine.

The woman is a timepiece set by the man. Fantasy added to prepared, pre-measured existence. What else is there to put in the pancake batter for that little extra something...that umph... that...

And the children...

"Mama? Mama?" Footfalls searching the brick entryway, carpet of the dining room; tile of kitchen, wood of den, cement of patio. Finding her kneeling by her roses. "Mama."

She shields her eyes when she looks up at her son backed by the afternoon sun.

"Mama."

"Charles." She brushes her hair back under her bonnet and realizes she has her flowered gloves on. There is a line of grayish soil on her forehead now. "No clubs today? It's Wednesday. Isn't it Chess Club?"

"Mama."

"You'll have to take it more seriously than you have if you intend on beating your father," she says stripping off her gloves and sifting through the fine soil. "He's telling everyone how he's going to fairly win the trophy.

"Mama."

"No," she raises her hand again and absently drops it to her knees. Her knees suddenly ache and she reminds herself that she must look for one of those padded cushions. A giggle threatens to rise from the back of her throat, but she is looking up at her son's face and the bubble of laughter dies there, at the back of her throat. It blocks her breath for a moment. "No. That's Tuesdays. Chess Club. Yesterday." She drops her eyes to her roses. She's waited for thirty-six years to have her own roses in her own garden. She shifts her knees slowly but vigorously pulls on her glove.

"Mama...?"

She hasn't asked after his day. Was it good? She had held him in a calm moment after his birth and had imagined asking him bout his test and projects and friends; asking him all of this in her rose garden, in the shade, with cool lemonade waiting on a nearby white, wrought iron table. A round table with an um...

"Mama."

Here is the garden. Here is her son. The table, round and strong and shaded, is there. But, already, the numbing shock that had dulled his eyes and brought back his toddler's cry of "Ma-Ma" was reaching her, dissolving the possibility of lemonade and light conversation. The soil on her fore head looks like ashes when she pushes her hat back. She sighs and begins to stand as he ways in a rushed wail, "Mama, they called me 'nigger'."

"What's a nigger?" Audwith wanted to know.

The man stared at his hands on the table. The woman gnawed at her upper lip. Guenever pulled at her hair ribbons. Beck hid her mouth with a milk glass. And Audwith repeated, "What's a nigger?"

Charles swallowed great quantities of food, keeping his mouth full and his brain empty. He ate like food would be his salvation. He'd discovered that inside his head, chewing was loud enough to drown out all other sounds.

Nigger must be really bad, Audwith thought. "What's a nigger, Mommie?"

His mother looked as if she might fling her plate at him. Instead, her hand clawed its way up to her face and she hid her wet eyes behind it.

Seeing no answer there, Audwith turned. "Dad..."

"What? Why? Is it like a Jap?" Audwith had once called a boy that because he had heard older boy say it. He had not understood his father's arrival at school—his old school—nor had he understood his father and his teacher—his old teacher, now the one who laughed so delightfully when she flung herself up over the double ropes turning, but the old teacher, at the old school, when they lived in the old town-house where the strangers Dad called the tenants now lived. She, his old teacher, had looked at him with narrowed eyes and clam shell mouth and had asked him to repeat something in his father's pretense. He had known they'd only get mad when they heard him say it and he wondered why they wanted to be mad and have all that red, tight feeling inside. He hadn't understood that. But, "Nigger must be like Jap, huh, Dad?"

Dad was staring above Charles' head.

"Huh, Dad? It must be like..."

"Yes!" All turned to the harsh scream of the woman. She apologized with a stretched out hand that reached for and touched nothing. "Yes, honey—Audwith. It's like Jap—mean and cruel."

Well, Audwith thought spearing a chunk of beef Guenever had sliced for him, Jap meant Japanese. Same difference, only you weren't suppose to say it. It wasn't nice. He studies Charles, his brother who ate and ate. That little boy had been Japanese. So, Charles, are you a nigger?

The woman screamed without a word of apology. Throwing her napkin to the table, she stood and ran out and up the stairs upsetting So-Comfort, who mewed loudly and scrambled across the dining room. The man stood also. He looked at Audwith. He looked at Charles, who also looked at Audwith with lips tightly sealed to hold back the mouthful of food. The man looked at the door. His eyes were incredibly fierce. His nostrils flared. He pointed to the ceiling. "Up, young man, up!" He bit the words but did not chew them. He did not spit them out. He held them in his mouth so that they pouched out his cheeks and dribbled over his chin, "Up! Dress for bed! Now!"

Audwith considered that. It was another thing you do without reason. He sighed and slid from his chair. "Good night."

The man bellowed, calling him back. And Audwith considered this also, one foot on the bottom step. He sighed once more and returned. The man stared at him. All those words seemed to be knotting his tongue and he could not say them. "Go away," was all he got out. "Upstairs."

Audwith turned once more with "Good night." He paused on the first stair, waited and listened. Finally he pulled himself up with the help of the banister. Midway up, he felt Beck behind him. He stopped. She gained the stair one lower and they went on, one for one. Outside her door, Beck tugged at his arm pulling him to a half.

"Audwith, what's nigger?"

Audwith shrugged. "Well," he heard his mother's voice, her on-the-phone voice. He heard the murmur of his father's voice, as reassuring and as rational as the man's who led you on the darkest rides at Disney World. He heard Guenever starting up the stairs. Some type of jump rope song was coming up with her, but not a double dutch. It was a single rope turning just plain—not with "grace and rhythm and fin-esse" like the ones his teacher sang. This teacher wouldn't ask him to say something she really didn't want to hear. She'd just say, "Audy, Audy, Audy," and smile. And that would be enough because he'd never dare say any word again that might erase that smile. He looked at Beck. "I guess it's something you are but don't want anybody to know that you are one. Like being Catholic, only worse. You don't want anybody to guess that you are one."

"It must be somethin' real bad."

"*Something.*" Guenever corrected on her way to her room. "Something, Beck. Don't hook the 'g' on your tongue. Let it out." She whirled haughtily away, braids floating after her with some rudimentary grace, style...finesse.

Beck ran her tongue cautiously against her upper teeth trying to feel the little 'g' surely hanging there by its tail.

The house...

It settled for the night. The wood rat gnawed and bounced against the pink insulation which should have killed him long ago. He was resourceful though and had mutated above its powers. So-Comfort, the car, curled and flicked out his claws. Occasionally he thought of the rat upstairs, but it was so warm down below. Harry, the fish, died sometime that night and floated up to the top of the bowl, This was something he had considered doing all his short life but had never before been able to accomplish basking in air.

Beck slept unaware of her parents' separate visits. Each pulled up her blanket, smoothed her cheek, kissed her hand and contemplated taking That Bear of Audwith's into hibernation.

Guenever dreamed she was in a candy store with Tonya—yesterday's best friend—and Angela. They ate a canister of chocolate-covered jelly beans with caramel centers. This heaven was spoiled by a giant, pink toothbrush that chased them out, yelling, "Bad, bad children! Bad! Bad!"

Charles tossed and turned with his father's words, "What does it say there? What does it say? Right there...read it. You are not a nigger. You are not stingy; you always share. You are not miserly; you always give. And a name cannot hurt you. A word is only as good as the person who uses it. Used ignorantly, it is an ignorant word. It is...silly." Charles had listened to this. But, in his head, in his dreams, he kept seeing the fifth definition.

And Audwith lay on top of his spread. He held his head up with the palms of his hands. He faced the window and the moonlight. Knees bent, feet swinging, he hummed a double dutch song.

The man and the woman laid in their bed. Every noise sent the man to the window, to pull aside heavy drapes and sheer linings, to lift a shade expecting to see crucified flames. Only confidence in his routine stayed him from running downstairs to check the front door's bolts every time he heard a sound.

It was only the wood rat; gnawing, gnawing, bouncing and gnawing.

Interlude

Early unnatural
morning
you awaken
to my crisp

crinkled laughter
as I motion to
your gracious
morning kisses,

as we lie etched
dark against
each other

while sunrise
slowly lingers
to break
the day...

Of last night's
kisses turbulent,
unspent

to warm me when
I'm exhausted,

my head weighted
down with dreams
when lovers mate

which enclose me
chocolate covered.

On the Levee

"Hundreds of strong black backs and arms
drawn from Mississippi farms
to work as dirt-carriers,
building river barriers.
Mule-drivers' wages a dollar six-bits a day;
and sometimes you didn't get your pay.
White boss-man,
sitting on his horse and brandishing a whip,
wore a gun on his hip.
If you didn't get paid, you didn't complain:
He'd just as soon put a bullet in your brain
as give you a 'Good-Afternoon'."

And the old man, swearing his story was true,
set me high on his shoulders so I could see the view.
And I felt a cold shiver:
I could still see the tracks of the mule drivers' wagons
down by the river.

Revelations

Word has it
that my father's father spent long years in prison.
Some "good ol' boys," out for a thrill,
were looking for a nigger to kill.
Grandfather tried to escape them
by shutting himself in an empty box-car,
but they rushed him too fast.
He had the door's iron bar in his hands,
and he struck the first to burst in upon him,
struck him until he was dead.

My mother said
that once some white-robed Klansmen
staked and burned a man.
So near it was
she saw and smelled the smoke,
and heard his screams.
She covered her ears;
and still she heard them,
long after he was dead.

Woman

In her genesis there is

    Passion, so rhythmic, so strong it
        holds one ever enthralled.
    Spirit, forged in mother's furnace, shaped
        on His anvil.
    Fertility obtained only in the Blackest soil
        of Eden.

    Created of his rib.
    Carved of the deepest mahogany,
    Ascending, graceful limbs, long and slender.
    That daintily sway upon her curved, ample
        form.
    Nubian eyes afire, burning, penetrating
        like the sun.
    Lips, moisten and full, RIPE!
    Head regally crowned with soft lamb's wool.
    Breast on which the world will suckle.

    A woman that is Africa,
    That is Eve,
    That is you.

It Ain't Sunday Till the Sun Rise

The cool blue-blackness of dawn
Envelopes a catacomb of warm funk,
Sin's sole witness.

An excuse for unmet eyes
As britches and brogans
Are slipped on with church prayer quietness.

Spent passion whispers,

"I don't know ya' on the street.
Hope to see ya' tomarra' at Sunday meetin'."

The cool blue-blackness of dawn
Envelopes the footsteps
From man to Mr. at the pulpit.
The gray Sunday suit
The patented face of day.
A race to beat tomarra' home.

Chuckling,

>   it ain't Sunday
>   it ain't Sunday
>   till the sun rise.

Holy Wars

*Marry women of your choice, two, or three, or four; but if ye fear
that ye shall not be able to deal justly (with them), then only one...The
Holy Qu'ran (Yusuf'Ali) 4:3*

Sharifa baked a coconut cake for the wedding and while it was
being eaten, she quietly left the mosque with her daughter
Malkia. She stopped by the house to get the suitcases she had
filled, then returned to the hall closet to await departure. She called her
mother to remind her of the arrival time and just as she returned the
phone to the receiver it rang. It was Hakim.

"Sharifa, why'd you leave?" he asked.

"That's a stupid question," she replied searching for the tirade
that had been fresh in her mind a second before.

"I thought we were together on this," he said. Sharifa didn't
reply. They held the phone in silence until Sharifa broke it.

"I'm taking Malkia and going to my parents, Hakim. You know
why and if you're disappointed, I really don't care. I'll call you in a few
days." She hung up the phone. She heard the phone ringing again as
she left the house.

While waiting for her flight to board, Sharifa wished she had
given Hakim her flight information. Maybe he would have come after
her with the intention of leaving everything else behind.

Three months ago, leaving him never would have crossed her
mind. They had settled into a good groove. Their bickering over money
stopped some months before when two more students joined Sharifa's
home-school and Hakim picked up a little side-income teaching Karate
at Gold's Gym. To celebrate, they had driven to Charleston to visit a
Muslim community that was growing on 200 acres of land just outside
the city. Hakim had relatives in Charleston, but insisted that they stay
near the Battery in a hotel room with a garden tub.

"You sure are being a sweety, Hakim. Like when we *first* got married," Sharifa said teasingly as they bathed together.

"Yeah, well you're a good girl so I think I'll keep you around," he
said without taking his eyes off of his wife's buoyant breasts.

"Okay, but you gotta give me another baby," she said straddling
him and kissing him wetly on the lips.

Their vocal lovemaking brought their 18-month-old, who had

been sleeping in the next room, into the bathroom where she stood unnoticed for several minutes. They laughed and pointed when they discovered her watching and she cried at being the butt of the joke.

On the drive back to Atlanta, they talked about the Muslim community. There wasn't much on the land, two large houses, and a 10 acre swath where fruits and vegetables grew. Sharifa was the first to mention the polygamous marriages that seemed to thrive within the community.

"I just can't see husband-sharing," Sharifa said, shaking her head. "I know its permissible in Islam, but it just doesn't seem right to me."

"It's natural," Hakim said immediately. "And those sisters seem to be reaping all the benefits," Hakim said. Sharifa looked at him with a raised eyebrow, but he didn't notice.

"Mmmm, I guess from a man's point of view it would seem natural. I can tell you though, you'd have a hard time with me if you tried that crap."

Hakim started to reply, but didn't. Sharifa studied his face trying to stare a response out of him, but he said nothing more until he spotted the Dairy Queen billboard and asked if she wanted ice-cream. The three of them shared french fries and a banana split.

The boarding announcement brought Sharifa back to the present. Malkia lay sleeping against her. She usually fell asleep that way each night as Sharifa read to her and then Hakim would carry her to bed. Angry tears welled in her eyes as she struggled to her economy-class seat with her daughter, the baby bag and her purse.

Fatima heard Hakim's Volkswagen pull into her driveway and she pulled the kitchen curtain aside to watch him approach the house. He was dressed in a white knee-length tunic with heavy embroidery around the neck and cuffs and matching punjab pants. He wore a white Kufi. His facial hair, a thick black mustache, goatee and full eyebrows glistened in the retreating sun and Fatima felt a tingling warmth rise in her stomach. "Mm, mm, mm," she said softly as she moved to meet him at the door while throwing a silk scarf around her graying braids.

Hakim had become a regular visitor in the last few months. Now that they had intentions to marry, he came without a chaperon. Besides, Shakir and Raheem, Fatima's sons, were always nearby. She had worked late that evening and ordered Indian food for dinner. The two of them sat in the kitchen putting off calling the boys in from their neighbor's Nintendo game until the food arrived.

"I'd like for you and Sharifa to meet soon," Hakim told her.

"I'd like that,' she replied hurriedly, then added, "should I invite her over here?"

Hakim didn't answer immediately, then shook his head. "No, I'm going to ask if she'll have you as a guest. You and the boys."

As if on cue, Shakur, followed precisely by his identical only smaller brother Raheem, rushed the kitchen.

"Brother Hakim," said Shakur, "we heard your car all the way down the street and knew it was you."

"Yeah, we knew it was you," echoed Raheem.

"Well, you all were right. It's me!" Hakim said standing and waving arms crazily in the air.

"Come on, show us how to do some more karate," Shakur said pulling Hakim towards the living room.

"Yah! Karate!" yelled Raheem half jumping off the floor in miniature sidekicks.

Fatima smiled at Hakim and shook her head as he was led away. Hakim winked back.

After spinach and goat cheese, tandoori chicken, saffron rice and naan, the boys said goodnight and headed for the bathtub. Hakim rose to leave and said he would call by the weekend with plans for her and Sharifa to meet. He called Sharifa his first wife and Fatima felt the startling insecurity that sometimes sucker punched her. She kept her back to him while rinsing the dishes and stacking them in the dishwasher.

At the door, Hakim brushed his hands along her folded arms and stood very close to her. Fatima did not look at him, feeling the uncomfortableness that precedes a first kiss. He did not kiss her.

"I know there are probably some things you are still getting used to," he said to her. He moved forward slightly as if to say more, but didn't.

She nodded, wishing he would kiss her, but instead, he let her go. He left her in the doorway, arms wrapped around herself.

Hakim told Sharifa what was going on before her own curiosity blossomed.

"I've made intentions on a second wife." The words came at her like a startling hallucination and she flinched. She felt like a windshield at the moment it is shattered by a brick.

"I know what you said about this before, Sharifa. You said you couldn't see polygamy for yourself. Right?" Again, she did not answer.

"Well, I'm asking you to trust my judgment. Islam provides guidelines and I believe I can adhere to them. I've kept you in mind all along. Sharifa?"

She wasn't listening, he knew. Her face had gone blank, then hard. He was always shocked that such a delicately formed woman could look so mean. She stood by the sink where she had just finished the dinner dishes. He knew she would say nothing until she was ready and then it might not be much.

She moved away from the sink and Malkia reached out for Sharifa to get her out of her high chair, but Sharifa ignored her. Sharifa stood staring at Hakim through narrowed eyes, arms wrapped around her waist.

"Hakim I know you're not serious. Cause if you are, you will have to divorce me first before you marry someone else. This isn't fuckin Egypt." Sharifa wiped Malkia's face and hands for a second time, then lifted her from her seat and handed her to Hakim.

"She needs a bath," she said, and added, "I'm sure you needed a cigarette when you sat down to figure out how you were gonna tell me this shit. Give me one." She held her hand out expectantly and Hakim had the urge to slap it out of the air.

"They're in my car. You can get them, but I want to talk about this some more. I'm serious."

Sharifa said nothing, just went to get a cigarette. Hakim frowned when he heard his car crank, but was not surprised. Sharifa had driven off before during arguments and returned hours later emotionally sedated. He knew she left because he didn't like it. He ran with Malkia to the front door to try and head her off as she pulled out of the carport, but she was already at the end of the driveway when he got to the door.

Hakim left the house before dawn hoping to make his first prayer of the day in the company of others. He lingered at the stop sign at the corner long enough to light a Newport. Of late, his habit that had materialized in the trenches north of Da Nang and disappeared when he kicked heroine two years after returning to American soil was resurfacing. Filling his lungs with smoke cut the edge.

Sharifa was his third wife. His first two marriages had ended from infidelity. He knew women well because they had always made themselves accessible to him. In his early years as a Muslim, Hakim had rationalized continuing his sexual forays as a single man's necessity.

Marrying Sharifa shed new light on his knowledge of matrimony. Their religious devotion gave their marriage boundaries. He respected her; she, him. He could depend on her. When he awoke her at night with his screams, she did not yell at him to "shut the fuck up," as his second wife had done, but held him until the possessive memories left him.

He did not want to hurt her, but was infuriated by her inability to trust him. She would not look at polygamy as anything but a personal affront. She believed that he was not happy with her. That she was not enough for him. That he wanted fresh pussy.

Her doubt fueled his own.

Fatima, on the other hand, was completely cooperative. Hakim could see in her eyes that she had been alone for some time. Her plumpness was probably a combination of late childbearing and loneliness. Her boys were a handful, too.

She was an attorney for the ACLU and did not need his financial support. She said she would trust him to balance his attentiveness to each family. Sometimes he feared the reality of a three-party marriage had not hit her. He had not left her bed yet to go home to his other wife.

The mosque was empty. Hakim had hoped Imam Ibrahim would be there early too so they could talk. He moved to the bookcase that sat in the rear of the men's prayer room and scanned book titles hoping something would grab him. Nothing seemed the antidote for his agitation so Hakim raised his hands in supplication and called out to his creator.

When Hakim mentioned nothing about remarrying for several days, Sharifa convinced herself the matter was forsaken. Plus, she had neither seen nor heard of any perspectives. She cooked him lamb chops, creamed spinach and corn on the cob, one of his favorite meals and told him over dinner she would run him a bath and give him a massage later.

Hakim decided then it was a good time for Sharifa to meet Fatima.

"I'd like to have Sister Fatima and her boys over on Saturday, Sharifa. Is that okay with you?" he asked reaching out for the fresh lemonade she had just made and was handing to him.

When the glass stopped mid-air, he knew his timing was bad. Sharifa involuntarily sucked her teeth and cut her eyes at him. Her apricot complexion turned plum. She set the glass carefully on the table, picked Hakim's unfinished plate from in front of him, dumped the contents in the garbage, and left the kitchen flicking off the light. Malkia used the cover of darkness to throw her dish to the floor.

Upstairs, Sharifa sat rigidly on the bed trying to hold all of her emotion inside.

That motherfucker is serious, she thought. "I can't believe his black, screamin' in the middle of the night ass."

She sat until the thought she tried desperately to hold back broke through. Tears ran hot and fast down her face and her body caved inward from the force of her silent sobs. The next morning after Hakim left to teach his morning Tai Kwan Do class she called Delta and purchased a ticket to D.C.

Fatima and Sharifa's first meeting was cordial. Sharifa was guarded, but an excellent hostess. Fatima hugged her as she left, Sharifa's arms remained limp at her side.

The wedding would be in three weeks. Sharifa confirmed the date on her standing reservation with Delta and planned to close her school a few weeks early. She didn't tell Hakim she was leaving mostly because she did not want to hear him stand by his intentions to have Fatima.

The summer months passed and Sharifa did not return home. She and Hakim talked sparingly in the first two months, then at least once a week. Hakim flew up to D.C. for Labor Day Weekend. Only when he undressed her did he notice the swell in her stomach.

On the Sunday before the holiday, the three of them picnicked in Rock Creek Park and later Hakim and Fatima listened to Jazz in Ft. Dupont Park leaving Malkia with her grandparents.

"So, how are you and Fatima working things out?" Sharifa asked reluctantly.

"Well, it's a little rough. She feels guilty for our split up and is kind of detached."

"I guess that's why you came up here after me? You getting lonely."

"I been lonely since you left. I miss you," he said. "I miss seeing my little girl get bigger and I wish you would come home so we can get it ready for our next little one." Hakim moved toward her on the blanket and lay his head in her lap. After a moment, Sharifa began running her fingers through the smooth hair that cupped his chin. They sat quietly until the last jazz note bowed out to the chorus of crickets.

Expressions of Black Love
in Black Food

Man say, "Girl, when I wake up in the morning, you're the:
    Syrup to my Flapjacks
    Eggs to my Grits
    Links to my Cream of Wheat
    Honey to my Biscuits
    Jelly to my Toast
    Cream to my Coffee
    Ice to my Milk
    And the Sugar to my Grapefruit"

Woman says, "Boy, when I get home in the evening, you're the:
    Cornmeal to my Catfish
    Fat to my Chittlins'
    Hogmaw to my Cabbage
    Onions to my Collard Greens
    Black Eyed Peas to my Rice
    Butter to my Cornbread
    Lemon to my Ice Tea
    And the Peaches to my Cobbler"

They both say, "Now ain't we in love!"

Waiting

Waiting
We sat in the evening sun, like statues
Hunched over our checkers/cribbage/bid whist table
Conversation flowing about the good ol' days

Waiting
Saw the beautiful lady pass, heads turned
Police cars raced down the street, sirens wailed
As the little old lady's purse was snatched

Waiting
Bill collector stopped at Mrs. Wilson's, who's not
at home
Detectives looking for Bud Wilson, who's not at
home
Moving company arrived, since they're not at home

Waiting
Saw the neighborhood change to a project
Shops closed as stores relocated to the suburb
Children board busses for their education

Waiting...

Diasporan Blues

I am caught up
In two worlds,
One I am familiar with,
One I am certain exists,
One that I conform to,
One that I try to dismiss.

They tell me that I am
From Africa,
They call it
The "Land of the Black,"
I now find myself on,
Diasporan grounds,
Too frightened to try and
Look back.

I find it much easier
To say that
I am "American,"
I avoid the stigmatization
That comes with saying that
"I am African."

My mother tells me that,
I have blood of,
"Indian," English, French,
Spanish, German, Italian,
And,
Jew,
She too says that,
I am "American,"
So what is my lost soul,
To do?

My family laughs at my,
Curiosity,
My friends say,
I must be insane,
My teachers teach me,
The half-truth,
I only want to know,
My name.

My grandmother despises,
African people,
And wherever,
Africans roam,
My grandfathers appalled at,
Our history,

Yet he insists,
Leave well enough,
Alone.

I have searched,
And,
Have searched,
And,
I have searched,
For my ancestry,
No one understands that,
I feel so alone,
No one listens,
When I speak about,
Africa,
No one cares that,
I'm trying to get home.

Survival

We engaged in dangerous games,
then—played in "The Pit."
And we got down.
But, I often carried the night
on my shoulders,
up against stars that wouldn't budge.
That Bank of America Building loomed,
it's capitalist's shadow
crushing dreams I dared to have.

Chant for Oblivion

you alabaster oppressor
      aborter of unborn rainbows.
you evil incarnate slug—
      spreading ooze over earth.

you slimy odious creature.
you maggot.
buzzard.
you beast.

you alabaster oppressor
      wrecker of rhythm.
you appropriator of culture(s)—
      weakening the pulsating beat.

you violent prone mutant.
you germ.
deceiver.
you whitemare.

you alabaster oppressor
      with power for a penis.
(looter.
landgrabber.
resource/mineral bandit.
despoiler of nature.
warmonger.
racist.
capitalist.
greedy muthafucker).

you dick-head—
afraid of pussy.

misery makes you hard.

You Dream of Flying

Y ou've started smoking again, and now you can't stop. After all these years, after all those warnings, you still don't pay attention, do you?

You've just had sex. The newest member of the human race exists, almost. But not yet. There. She's one cell, now. She's drifting.

You look around your tiny bathroom and see how the paint is scrubbed to a dull gray, but it's better than the hairy black mold that would be growing if you didn't clean constantly. Then you look into the mirror at your unlined face, and still don't believe in the sincerity of those who believe that you are attractive. You rub your thick mop of hair and shake your head slightly. You pick up a comb to scratch your scalp, your roots are coarse and kinky. But first you take a long drag off of your Virginia Slim. Here's to coming a long way, baby.

Just now, across town, a meeting has come to order. Strategies about bad publicity that they, the pro-lifers, have been getting lately. They want to save that life inside you. They want her to live in this world, not too close, though, not in their neighborhood, cavorting with their own perfect, pink, above average children. This is their curious, secret shame. Why do you tell yourself these things that you don't want to know? Because this is the world, part of your life. You need to read the papers more.

You're in the shower, and the young one is, what do you think, four cells now? Perhaps, you consider. But the people across town have high hopes for her. Her? She hasn't got a vagina. Hell, she hasn't got a face. Still, those double x chromosomes, they chant out her future, like a choir of thousands, SHE SHE SHE SHE SHE, as they duplicate.

In your bedroom, your gladdened sperm donor is heavy lidded, his eyeballs rolled upward like a baby's, already in that dreamscape that men go to after sex. He looks too perfect when he's asleep. You met him a week and a half ago at the diner where you work, and already, the things that attracted you to him, his eyes, his hair, his body, are getting real old because now all you see when you look at him is a dummy. A big, dumb, shallow airhead, who growls at you when you don't want to watch sports on TV. He doesn't believe that women have sexuality, not really, and he didn't hold you, he didn't wait for you, and your orgasm never made it, and you hated him a little bit, admit it, just for a minute. When you said, *yes it was good,* when he asked, *how was it.* You did hate him just then, didn't you?

You're in bed and you lie on your back, and think about the condom. You think of the hell, the catastrophes that can follow when it fails you. It's too scary to think about for too long. But still, you think of how the thing can alter your fate. And take your life and turn it more inside out than it already is. Yes it does. You think of a piece of latex, so thin and flimsy it's silly. And so powerful. You think of how the thing doesn't always take hold of those quick hands of fate. It just doesn't always, well, perform.

Now its dark inside your bedroom, and a red light blinks into your room from outside. You're thinking that you might be getting scared, but you don't want to scream, you don't want to look silly, for nothing. But something is moving, yes? Something evil is moving on the ceiling? You stare, you can't be sure. Sure. It's a cockroach, coming out from behind a piece of cracked paint, and now she's wiggling her antennae at you because it's a test. She wants to know if you can see her. She freezes when you reach to click on the light, and does a last ditch circling dance when you jump up and shoot her with hair spray. She falls for what has to be a hundred cockroach feet. After a hundred foot fall, you or me, we would have been all blood and bone, sister. But this greasy insect, she shakes and staggers over onto her stomach, drops an egg packet in her death throes, and marches away across the blankets. That is when you start to believe that if you do go mad one day, it will definitely, yes, most definitely be because you want a life without cockroaches. You want it so badly that you cry now, and your lover is awake and saying, "What the fuck? What the fuck?"

First you change the blanket, then you fall off into sleep. Your child has grown, she's eight cells, now. Dream sweet, you do deserve it, this vacation.

It's morning, it's seven a.m. But you're already working because your life isn't like the coffee commercials on TV. The dishwasher says what she always says to you, "Working hard today?" Her mouth is always skewed to one side. Always. You're a smart person so you fascinate her. But you don't smile back at her, do you? It's so hard, working with someone so soft, so stupid. She turns your workday into a bad, slow-motion dream. You must talk to her slowly as you move very fast. How can you do your job when the clean dishes never come fast enough, when the tables aren't ready? You hate the new dishwasher a lot, don't you? You know you do.

It's the people who come in, the butt crack men, you call them, secretly. When they summon you by wiggling their empty coffee cups at you, you think, it's the damn people who make the place cheap. And lately, you notice, they leave you lousy tips because the service is slow, because the dishwasher gets distracted every time she sees shiny earrings, or pretty, pretty bracelets.

You go to the table that the dishwasher is hovering over. You interrupt her empty moment by clearing the table for her so quickly, that now she's confused. She stares at you, head cocked, then picks up a cup and nervously wipes it, and this wiping, it calms her, and now she can think again. "Working hard today," she says, "so are you!" She stares at you so helplessly that you want to scream, because you feel so evil, don't you?

Your bodymate, deep in your womb, doesn't sense your offensive emotions, she has no nerve cells, not yet. Just now, across town, her father is at the unemployment office, talking to a civil servant with two years until retirement, and a bottle of whiskey in a file cabinet marked "Miscellaneous." Her father, your lover, makes up the places that he's been to find a job. And back in your apartment, your cat, Trixie, watches through a window. She watches with her big green eyes, and for a moment, she almost looks intelligent. A dove is making a nest outside on the broken fire escape. Trixie has white puffs on the tip of each foot that look like adorable woolen mittens. She folds her teeny feet under her, then she closes her eyes softly and dreams of murder. You don't know this, of course you don't. It's just another long day. But it's time for your break. You take a long drag off of a cigarette, and your embryo slows its ravenous division, just a tad.

You see the dishwasher stealing a tip. You pry the dollar out of her hand and threaten, very softy. First. she starts moaning and swaying, then she doesn't move again for quite awhile. You say, "I mean it, Wanda, I'll come to that nut farm you live at and eat your goldfish while you watch." The dishwasher moves in slow motion as she stacks dishes into the washer, and cries for her fish, Harvey and Lulu.

Weeks go by, and you're lying on your back in a public clinic. You've always known about her, your body companion. You knew the condom was no good, and when you asked the druggist, he said, "Kids. Kids," he repeated, "poked pin holes in the condoms for fun, for joy." Then, he clicked his tongue and narrowed his eyes at you. "People don't know how to raise kids anymore," he shook his finger, with his chin in the air. "Women are too busy being liberated!" He feels he must rant, he feels he's allowed. You've known him for years. He's stupid, he's old. But you don't forgive him.

Today, no one is holding your hand. The nurse is staring at your old faded clothes lying in a heap in a corner of the chilly white room. When you look up, mostly you just see the bottom of her flappy chin, but you do see some of her pale, small eyes. The smell of antiseptic makes you squirm, then you hear some squeaking footfalls as someone else approaches. Just for you, the nurse above you with the liver spots on her jowls begins to talk about her son as she starts the I.V. "He's in law school, you know," she says. You see the other one give a big, slow, nod of approval, then look down at you. She smiles quickly when she catches you looking at her. Her smile is the one that she practices for the people she deals with on this job. You want for them both to have strokes, right now, the bitches.

Something about being so alone at this moment makes you pissed, but mostly you know you're scared that this will be what finally does it. That this day, this clinic, this deed, and not cockroaches, will summon you to the edge, and over. But what's a girl to do? What, or who, will save you? Just one wish, that's all you want, that's all you've ever wanted, for just one wish, one lousy dream to come true. But no, damn it all to hell. Damn it to hell, because no one ever told you it would be like this, that your wants, your hopes, were some silly, flimsy, useless things. Were they? Yes, you know they were. No. You don't know that, not really. Not entirely.

As the drugs pull you under, you hear the pro-lifers outside protesting. One voice, high and shrill with fury is screaming over, and over, "Its a baaybeeeee! Its a liiiiiife! God maaaade it! Don't Doo-oo-oo-oo-oo-oo it!" You begin to hate...no...pity. You begin to pity the woman behind that voice.

You dream of flying.

Thirteen

Six times the stupid stuff came up with the same stupid color.

positive, positive, positive, positive, positive, positive

Maybe I'm not reading the directions right. Right? I just want one box to say I wasn't, you know. Maybe these EPT things don't work. Like, what if they are all wrong? I mean, what if the people who mixed up the stuff that day, came to work sleepy, because they stayed up watching the Arsenio Hall show or something, and weren't paying attention? I did that once and failed a math test, and I'm smart. What if the direction thing is wrong? What if the secretary lady who writes this stuff on all the boxes messed up? I had a White teacher who wrote the wrong names down for detention, so I know grown-ups are really stupid, you know.

I can't be, you know, that. I mean, I've only got my period five times, so it's not possible. Right? You have to be real old, like seventeen, or something. Or a bad girl, like Pee-Wee down the street. And besides, I only did it once, for about a minute. Or two. And I didn't take all my clothes off like they do in the movies, so it's almost like I practically didn't do it, right? And besides, we were standing up, so all the yucky, sticky stuff ran back out of me. And anyway, I didn't like it. That has to count for something, you know. It really hurt. I mean, I don't see what all the fuss is about. He wanted to, and I didn't want him to think I didn't like him, so, you know. And he is so fine, he has his hair cut real short on the sides and long on the top with wavy lines around both sides and he raps and he can dance better than anybody. He won first place at the school African-American dance. All the other girls like him, but he says he likes me. So there. He said if I wanted to be his girlfriend, and wanted to go to Sherrie's birthday party with him, I had to, you know. Do it. Well I didn't have to, but it would help our relationship, he said. He said he wouldn't tell anybody. I said cool.

. . . .

I've been totally puking early in the mornings. I've got to lay off that Mexican food. It makes me run for the border.

. . . .

I didn't get my "friend" this month either. So, now that's twice. I wonder if when it first starts, if it like skips a while then comes back? You know, like it takes a vacation or something. I hope it does, anyway. I stole some more money from mom's purse and I bought some more EPT test things.

....

positive, positive, positive, positive, positive, positive

....

I am so scared. I have not seen him since that day we did it behind the bleachers. He hasn't called, and he hasn't stopped by my locker like he used to between lunch and fifth period and he didn't even take me to Sherrie's party. Jerk.

....

I saw him today. Total JERK. He was with his friends and when I walked up they all called me "Boot Knockin' Bleacher Girl." Jerk. He must have told them we did it behind the bleachers in the gym. Such a tattle tale. Then they ran off laughing. He lied to me. I cried. I wrote him a letter and stuck it through the holes of his locker and told the scum that I'm pregnant. I told him he better call or I'll sue him and make him get a job at Burger King.

....

A guy named Akeem called me. I stuck the note in the wrong locker.

....

My mom asked me if I was pregnant. She has been counting my period pads, and she said she "happen to notice" I haven't been using any. Such a snoop. Always acting like she's so concerned about me so she can dig in my business, you know?

Always tripping off something, you know. Besides, like, it's not even any of her business. Just because she's a nurse she thinks she knows everything there is to know about everything.

....

I saw him today on lunch. I was with Melissa and Lorna and we were talking about which one of us was going to marry Wesley Snipes and who was going to marry Denzel Washington. We were eating fish-sticks, because it's Friday and it's a Catholic thing, you know. Which totally confuses me because I'm Baptist. But I don't go to church, so it's kind'a like I'm Catholic, I think. Anyway, I walked over to the Jerk and tried to talk to him, you know, and this cheerleader bitch walked over and stood between us and asked me why was I talking to her boyfriend. Such a bitch. I told her excuse me, but he's like my boyfriend, because like we have been totally sexual you know. We have a commitment, okay.

She said that they were sexual, too. I said, for sure. Copycat. You just said that because I said that. Then I lost it and told him, "Besides, I'm carrying your child, so that should give me some priority over some pom-pom carrying, cart wheel flipping, cheer screaming for a losing team, cockeyed, dread-lock wearing, Yo-Yo wanna be, bitch, you know." He said WHAT? so I had to repeat myself. Then I walked off like they do in the soap operas. Neat, huh? I felt so mature because I used the word "priority" correctly.

Cool, huh?

Jerko keeps calling me. He wants to know if I'm really pregnant.

My mom keeps bugging me. She wants to know if I'm really pregnant.

My mom took me to the doctor today. I'm really pregnant.

My dad called today. He knows I'm really pregnant.

I'm scared because I'm really pregnant.

. . . .

My dad flew in today. We all went over to the Jerk's house to talk with the Jerk's parents. Me and the Jerk didn't even look at each other. El Jerko looks so different at school, you know. At school he looks so cool, so with it, now he looks like a total wimp. So uncool. And I never even noticed he had a greasy face and pimples. Gross! He needs to totally Oxidize. I'm so glad I didn't kiss him. Anyway, my mom keeps crying and squeezing my hand. Such a waste. My dad did most of the talking. Mr. and Mrs. Jerko asked Jerko Junior if he did the wild thing with me. He stalled, then he said "Yeah." Then my parents asked me if I was doing it with any other boys, and I screamed "Not even. Like, I'm not a slut, okay?" I wanted to die, I mean, they are so stupid, right? They made me wait in the car and Jerko was sent to his room while the "adults" had a discussion.

. . . .

This morning, after she took Dad to the airport so he could fly back home, Mom asked me what "we" wanted to do about it. I asked her why didn't dad tell me bye. She didn't answer.

. . . .

I didn't go to school today. Mom and Mrs. Jerko took me to the next city this morning. Mom drove. They brought Jerko Junior along. I got an abortion. Mom put it on her American Express. Almost three hundred dollars. I didn't know you could charge something like this. It was so, scary. All those weird totally wacko people standing out front pushing pictures of what they said were "aborted feet of us" in our faces. Gross. They look just like dead babies. Like, isn't that the stuff that old people call pornography or something? Shouldn't they like be at work or something? So immature. Like, get a life, please. They even had the nerve to follow us up to the front door of the place. They kept pointing in our faces and telling my mom that she shouldn't get an abortion, and if she did she'd go to hell, and like, she's not even pregnant. Stupid.

When we came back out they spat at us and started shouting nasty things. I cried and I was walking funny because that metal thing the doctor used hurt. It was cold and gross. Everybody in the office kept looking at me and shaking their heads. I heard some woman say "so young." Not even. I'm almost fourteen, in two years I can get my drivers permit, get a good job at McDonald's and support myself, so I'm practically an adult, right? Nobody said anything on the ride back. Jerko's mom jerked out her jerky colored checkbook wrote my mom a check when we stopped in front of Jerkville Manor, then Jerko and Momma Jerko just got out of the car. Jerko slammed the door. They didn't even look back or say good-bye, not that it mattered. I thought he liked me. Anyway. Jerko saw some of his friends coming down the street and he ran to play football. When I got home, I thought Mom would be real mean and scream at me after what happened, but she went into her room and closed her door. She was in there a long time. I think she was crying. I cried, too. Then I slept all night.

. . . .

I heard Jerko transferred to another school, and there is a rumor going around that the cheerleader bitch is pregnant.

. . . .

Today my mom had a "long talk" with me about safe-sex and birth control and stuff like that. I never noticed, but she's really sort'a kind'a smart. I told her I was sorry and I wouldn't do that again until

I'm married or real old like she is. Mom laughed and said that she doesn't think I'll wait until I'm twenty-seven. I told her she was right, I'd probably die of old age way before then. I don't know why she thought that was so funny. She told me she was sorry, too, for what I don't know.

. . . .

I never noticed this before, but Mom's kind'a neat for a grown up. We've been talking a lot lately. About nothing special, just talking. Today I dressed up like Mom, she thought it was "cute." Same colors and everything. Then we went out to Baskin Robbins for a waffle cone and then she like took me to a movie and then we went to the mall and played some video games. Totally cool, huh? I even let her win a few. Everybody thought we looked like sisters, so I told everybody I was her sister. She winked at me and she told everybody I was her sister. She said I was her best friend. I liked that. Cool.

The Mothers

Mrs. Laverne Barkley, mother of Elliott James Barkley, 21 years old, killed while at Attica prison, September 13, 1971.

and

Mrs. Gussie Mae Love, mother of Joetha Collier, 18 years old, shot to death in Drew, Mississippi, by 3 drunken White men, May 16, 1971.

and

Mrs. Fannie Lee Chaney, mother of James Chaney, 21 years old, who was lynched, along with Andrew Goodman and Micheal Schwerner, during "The Mississippi Summer" of 1964.

and

to all African-American Mothers whose children are being destroyed by violence.

How
is that my child
head flying apart
life smeared across the gray coldness?

how
when only yesterday/this morning
his eyes questioned mine
& his mouth touched the rim of this cup

see
here are the prints of his fingers
jellied and dirty
there are his socks
soaked with his sweat
under his hat.

But
here we stand
carved out of ebony/clay
stomach dropping in fear
sweat glistening cold on our palms

as
pain knifes
twists
rises higher & higher
blinds our eyes
flares our nostrils
as
we suck in air
trying to relieve
to disbelieve.

How
is that my child?
smooth charcoal legs firm
loins fertile for first child
of her own

flattened
into a yellow chiffon
red blood covered
still life.
twisted & bent
in a no/life pose
cheek touching grass
eyes half-mast.

But
again we're standing
weathered knuckles bent
clutching fists of futility
closing over the empty night air

as
the beat throbs
moves up to our mouths
as we scream
silently

then
loudly
pushing the sobs
out up
over the screams of the sirens.

How
is that my child?
bar patterns across his face
telling of his missed youth

eyes
curved up
toward the sound of guard/feet
detention bells

flicker
one beat
rinsing out remembrance
close quick-silver
re-emerges whites only

as
he reels backward
slumps
kneels

&
then a slow motion
STOP.

That is not our child
laying form changed
in the grass
on the street
in a cell. That is not our child...NOT OUR CHILD...NOT...

BUT
PLEASE
TELL ME WHY
WHY WAS THAT OUR CHILD???

Black Dilemma

As of yet...
    we're still waiting...
...hand and ear...glued to the door...
too afraid that just maybe...
...the door's not locked anymore!

The harvest will feed our cravings...
...seeds planted...generations before...
Yet we sit patiently awaiting...
...who the heck...are we waiting for?

Aren't we sick and tired...being thought lazy?
...uninspired...of course ignored!
Big Surprise!!!...perception's kind of hazy...
...only Clark Kent...sees through doors!

Perhaps, who knows...maybe...
...opportunity's knock...is battle-worn!

Could it be, Dear Ones
    we're yet awaiting...
      ...the key to an "unlocked" door?

Trinidad

Oh Trinidad, why do I love you so?
Why do I see your virtues,
While others see your faults?
Why do I see your beauty while others
    only see your ugliness?
I love you for so many reasons;
Too numerous to list.
However, I'll try.
I love you because you are you,
A unique gem in that chain of Caribbean jewels.
I love you because you are the land of my birth and my roots are deeply
    embedded in your rich soil and culture.
Twenty-seven years, girl; that's a long, long time.
No wonder I dream of you daily.
Family, friends, neighbors are dear to me.
They provide me with points of reference,
An appreciation of growth and decline,
    space and time, of life and death.
They help me define who I am; where I came
    from; and where I'm going or would like to go.
Everybody likes to be somebody.
In Trinidad I am more somebody than
    anywhere else in the world.
I'm somebody's son, brother, uncle,
    godfather, ex-teacher, neighbor, cousin,
    friend, partner, husband and brother-in-law.
Yes, in Trinidad, I know I am somebody.
Love is very difficult to express in words.
Love should be acted out.
Words seem so inadequate;
So imprecise to describe my feelings and
    yearnings for you, my native land.
Suffice it to say: I love you Trinidad.
Trinidad, Trinidad, land of my birth.

As She Pushes

silken thighs
sweat film embracing
taut self
as she pushes
the rhythm of the pain
dances round her navel
as she pushes
screams of everywoman
fly found passive walls
as she pushes
hair turns back
muscles quiver
feet reject stirrup bounds
as she pushes
form into substance
self into shape
as she pushes
thought into void
sound into silence
as she pushes
Christopher into the world
screaming

Jazz Diva

i like it best when she swings into scat
triple fortissimo
experienced notes of power
distant thunder breathed in A minor
      or
whispers like shock waves
skin deep sounds of passionate pianissimo
tremblers
honey chords
riffs of vibration unleashed
    talk to me scat static
moans from every instrument
float on scores of E major
an ill wind hid that lush life
sassy Sarah
lady with a song

Spirit of the Streets

A ghost of a spirit
In a black body,
Curled among
Carton boxes.
The white of the
Eyes, glares.
Fragile life,
A skeleton of
Desire gone.
Human waste...
Someone's treasure
At some interval
Of time.
But now,
Shed, stepped over,
And kicked awake
By a passerby.
No bed of dreams
Does he rest on,
But he sleeps on
What reality walks upon.

Natural Causes

For years Laurel never understood why her mother had died. She tried to get the answer from her grandmother Carrie, but all she ever got were quotations from the Bible. "The Lord giveth, and the Lord taketh away, child. Now hurry and get dressed."

Every Sunday when Laurel was eight Grandmother Carrie and Aunt Amelia took her and her sister, Valle, to the cemetery to visit their mother's grave. Woodbalm Cemetery was on a steep hill that was visible from Grandmother Carrie's house. In the distance Laurel said she spied the cemetery beyond the tall buildings, over towering tree-tops, and through the morning fog; and Valle said she even glimpsed her mother's grave.

At the cemetery when Valle pointed out the tombstone, Laurel propped herself against the small granite slab as if it were a marble fortress. Valle was twelve. She had been four when their mother died and she thought she knew everything.

Every Sunday they'd come to the cemetery bringing skates, a blanket, lunch, roses and their mother's photo album; it was as if they were going on an all-day picnic.

Grandmother Carrie placed the picnic basket to the side of their mother's marker and spread her newly crocheted blanket. She set out peanut butter and jelly sandwiches, green apples, clover honey, and sweet potato pie. Her strong hands moved quickly, flashing the turquoise ring she had worn for the last forty years. It was so tight her lemony skin protruded above the gold band.

Widowed Aunt Amelia, plumper than she wanted to be, walked over and helped herself to a double slice of pie.

"Grandmother, will angels sing today?" Laurel asked.

"This afternoon, Laurel," she said. "I'll ask the organist to play the song that was played at your mother's funeral."

"Grandmother, what happened to our mother?" Laurel asked, as she always did when they came to the cemetery.

Grandmother Carrie, lost in thought, her hands folded like in prayer, stood at the foot of their mother's grave like an iron lady. Only her fingers trembled.

"Your Grandmother's not a weeper," said Aunt Amelia. "She's a warrior."

"Grandmother," Laurel asked again, "how did our mother die?"

"Laurel," Grandmother Carrie said. "I told you: the angels took her."

"But how did she die before they took her?"

"Without a whimper," Grandmother said, with a serene face. "We named your mother Victoria because we knew she'd be victorious. Had she lived she would have been the savior of our family."

The church organ began to play, and music filled the cemetery. Laurel walked down the steps that led down to a door buried in the hillside and entered the crypt where the organist was playing, gliding her fingers over the keys as if they had been waxed with butter. She played "Rock of Ages," "When the Morning Comes" and "It Is Well with My Soul."

Laurel pressed her face against the side of the organ, using all the powers of her fantasy to imagine how her mother would have saved Uncle Emory from polio, Aunt Ophelia from the train wreck, and Cousin Jake from that stroke of lightning. She wondered what her plan was to save Daddy from bourbon. She envisioned her like Sleeping Beauty, wondering how she could bring her back.

And since the whole family talked so often about Victoria, Laurel felt at times that her mother never had died.

"This is my baby sister's child," Aunt Amelia would tell the immigrant grocer, Mr. Jaffe, whenever they shopped in the deli. "You remember my sister Victoria?" she coaxed. "The one with the wavy black hair?"

They waited while Mr. Jaffe's wrinkled forehead and perplexed eyes probed the dark recesses of his memory.

"Remember my youngest sister? The one who died?"

Mr. Jaffe's eyes scanned the store, his eyes sank back in thought, groping desperately for some memory of that dark-haired sister. "I think I do remember her," he said.

Hearing the family talk of her mother was like hearing about a movie Laurel had never seen. People kept telling her different things as if she had been there. She wished she could have remembered hearing her mother's voice or touching her face just once.

"Grandmother, tell me that long word she died from again?" Laurel asked.

"Tuberculosis," Grandmother Carrie said, with sad eyes.

Laurel felt confused. Last week, in the back yard, Valle had yelled, "Liar! It's not true."

Laurel rushed outside and saw Valle flailing her arms at a neighbor girl's face.

"Your mother jumped out of that window," Yula said. "And my mummy *saw* her." She pointed to their living room window.

"Laurel, don't you believe her," Valle said, covering Laurel's ears.

"She hung on a nail," Yula insisted, until Valle socked her in the belly.

"Why do you fight if it's not true?" Laurel had asked Valle later.

"Because nobody's gonna lie about our mother," Valle had said, "and get away with it."

The organist had finished playing "It Is Well With My Soul," and Laurel opened her eyes and ran back up the steps. Aunt Amelia was helping herself to another slice of sweet potato pie.

"Mmm, this sure is good," she said.

Laurel looked at her, wondering if she knew anything about how her mother had died. As if reading Laurel's thoughts, Aunt Amelia blurted out, "When your father was Victoria's boyfriend, we chased him away with the broom." She lowered her big brown eyes to the ground, then sadly looked at Laurel. "None of our family liked your daddy, except me. At the funeral, your Aunt Ophelia screamed out at him, 'Murderer! He killed her. He killed our baby sister.' She crooned this, like some howling dog. It was the craziest thing I'd ever heard. Your daddy told me, 'If your family had let us alone, we could have made it. But no, I wasn't good enough.'"

"She should have married that preacher," said Grandmother.

Aunt Amelia cornered the last pie crumb with the prongs of her fork, glanced up at Grandmother Carrie and said, "You know that's why Victoria eloped and..."

Grandmother Carrie's look hushed her lips, sealed Laurel's ears with its silence. "Judge not, that ye be not judged," Grandmother Carrie said. "First cast the beam out of thine own eye; then shalt thou see clearly to cast out the mote from thy brother's."

Aunt Amelia shook her head. "Our family—God bless their souls—they won't let you live and they won't let you die."

Sprawled on the cemetery grass by her tombstone, Valle and Laurel turned pages of their mother's album—where each photo was glued with exactness.

"Baby Valle and Victoria on the steps of the Lincoln Memorial," they read. "Baby Valle with Aunt Amelia at Union Station. Baby Valle and Daddy at Thanksgiving. About 4:00; 4:23 to be exact."

In her pristine handwriting the inked letters were meticulously formed. Laurel longed to slant the h, lift the top off the t, pluck the dot from the i. Instead she kept turning pages. She knew there would be no picture of her mother with her.

"But what happened to my pictures?" she asked Grandmother. Looking through the album always made Laurel feel she didn't exist.

"Your mama got sick after you were born."

"Couldn't somebody take a picture of me?"

"The Lord is my shepherd; I shall not want," quoted Grandmother Carrie.

"Wasn't I special too?" Laurel shouted.

"The Lord works in mysterious ways."

"Why did the Lord let the angels take her away?"

"The Lord giveth, and the Lord taketh."

Laurel imagined her mother flying like a dove into the heavens. "Didn't she love me?"

"Of course, sweetheart," Grandmother Carrie said squeezing Laurel in her arms as if she could squeeze out the pain and cure the hole inside her. "Be still and know that you are a child of God."

Valle and Laurel mused over the pictures, coming to the last one in the book.

"Did she ever spank you?" Laurel asked.

"Once," said Valle, " but not hard."

"Did you cry?"

"A little, play tears."

Laurel watched Valle divide up the roses they'd brought, dropping the buds to the ground in two separate piles, one for the reds and one for whites, sneaking herself a couple of extras, the same way she dealt out the deck of Old Maid.

"Valle took more reds," Laurel shouted frantically.

"Now girls," Grandmother Carrie said. "Honor thy mother."

The girls rolled their skates under the nearby bench, knelt on the hallowed ground, kissed their mother's grave, then laid upon it red roses. Around the graves of their aunts, uncles, cousins and granddad, they placed white roses, offsetting their mother's grave, which, to Laurel, dazzled like a ruby mounted in a crown of diamonds.

"Grandmother, our mother's dead," Laurel said, wishing she could remember her the way Valle did. "Why aren't we using white?"

"Laurel, when Victoria was about your age she planted our red rosebush," Grandmother Carrie said, glancing toward their mother's stone as if it would speak. "She'd be pleased it's still blooming roses."

"Guess what, Laurel," Valle said, "over her casket was a wreath; a heart of red roses." An impish smile curved Valle's mouth, as if she were privy to some secret information.

"She's in glass, isn't she, Grandmother?" Laurel said, as if she had been there too.

"Yes, honey," Grandmother said, staring at their mother's tombstone. "Your mommy's preserved in a glass vault. If I were to open it, she would be the same as she was the day she died."

Laurel pictured her mother preserved like the red rose in the glass paperweight on top of Grandmother's Bible. Frequently she would gaze at her mother's picture in the bathroom mirror, holding her mother's portrait next to her face, searching for some resemblance to the golden angel whose fringed hair flanked the soft lines of her tranquil face, gentle mouth and dark oval eyes. She looked for a hint of the inner person, some semblance of her mother's soul beneath the polka dotted dress and demure smile, but the glossy face only smiled back at her.

Gathering a handful of red roses, Laurel tossed them across her mother's grave like pick-up sticks, interlacing them over her like a knitted blanket. "Lay them straight," Valle commanded.

"I don't have to," Laurel answered, lining up the long stems. "They're flowers, not soldiers. Besides, the wind will blow away the petals."

"Wide is the gate that leadeth to destruction...," Grandmother Carrie said. "Narrow is the way which leadeth unto life and few there be that find it."

Laurel wondered if she would be one of those few.

Suddenly Valle, with her dark, spiral curls, disappeared from the gravesites to the pavement, where she chalked hopscotch numbers on the sidewalk. Laurel joined her, threw a piece of glass on square two and hopped onto the number singing: "Daddy said one day we might have a new mother." She threw the glass to three. The beveled chip slid like ice tumbling into a crack in the sidewalk.

"She'll never be our mother," Valle said, picking up the glass to take her turn.

"She can still be our mother even if she didn't born us."

"No, she can't."

"Yes, she can. Tommy's mother didn't born him and she's still his mother."

"Can't." Valle pushed Laurel off the square.

"Can! Just because you're four years older than I am, don't think you know everything."

She and Valle had begged Daddy to let them live with Grandmother Carrie when he went back into the army. He had said they could, then jokingly, laughed, "You might even have a new mother when I come home."

"She won't marry you when she sees that great big tattoo," Laurel said, glancing at the rose tattoo spanning the inside of his chestnut arm like a badge. Above the petals, in bold capitals, were her mother's initials: VPMT, with the year of her birth and death, 1916-1941.

"Whoever marries me will have to marry her too," their father said, crossing his arm in front of his chest like a shield. He smoothed his palm over the tattoo. "She's the only woman I've ever loved."

Laurel's eyes lifted to his high cheekbones and sought the longing in his stare. From the tone in his voice Laurel knew the space left inside him was so tiny the next lady would have to be small.

At the bench where Grandmother Carrie sat, Laurel clamped on her skates and wheeled back over to the sidewalk. Skating across the squares, she cracked the piece of glass gleaming in square four.

"Go away or I'll tell," Valle yelled.

"Tattletale," Laurel called, skating through the middle of the game. She stooped down, took off her skate and rubbed the numbers with the side of her saddle shoes.

"I'll bet you're not even my real sister," Valle said with clenched teeth.

"I am too."

"You are not. Your eyes are too slanted."

Laurel buckled her skate strap, turned around, skated back and sat on her mother's grave, wishing she could tell her mother what a meany Valle was.

After lunch the girls skipped around the cemetery subtracting the birth and death dates on the tombstones. They danced around the graves singing: "Ring around the roses, pocketful of posies. Ashes, ashes, we all fall down." They fell on the grass and pretended they were dead.

All day, organ music floated from underground pipes, resounded, loud like a clarion call. Blades of grass swayed like trumpets. The glockenspiel chimed. Leaves fluttered in the warm breeze. Laurel fell asleep on the cemetery lawn and dreamed of her mother.

Laurel dreamt she was sitting on the steps beside her mother, explaining her homework. Her mother was huddled near the radiator, designing snowflakes. Her eyes were closed as they always were in Laurel's dreams. Laurel tried to pry them open. And then she was her mother, or at least her eyes were also closed.

When she awoke, she told Grandmother Carrie she dreamed she had died. "I sat up in the casket and looked out at our dead and living relatives. I was so happy to see you, Grandmother Carrie, Aunt Amelia and you, Valle."

Valle's eyes brightened like shiny coals. "Maybe you want to live underground."

Laurel's heart somersaulted.

The organist began the funeral song. A gold sun sneaked behind a purple cloud. Valle and Laurel inched closer to Grandmother Carrie on the concrete bench, singing, "He Touched Me." The song reminded Laurel of an incident Valle had fabricated: she said it was Laurel who with three other little girls had climbed to the top of the school's chain link fence while three boys below put their hands on their legs, scooted them up the fence and peeped under their dresses. Laurel liked and hated that song. For Grandmother Carrie had preached, "Nice girls don't allow little boys to touch them. Your mother was always a lady."

"Everybody makes her sound so perfect," Laurel told Aunt Amelia later.

"Well," said Aunt Amelia. "She was."

As they left the cemetery Laurel walked backwards, throwing her mother good-bye kisses, calling out, "See you in my dreams."

"I could have doctored Victoria better at home," Grandmother said, gazing back at their mother's grave.

"Stop playing God," said Valle, imitating Aunt Amelia. "There you go again, blaming yourself."

A well-respected midwife, Grandmother Carrie was known for her home remedies: whiskeyed rock candy, sassafras roots, camphorated oil. To cure her colds, she would pin a flannel plaster to Laurel's undershirt. The salve heated her chest and hugged her like melted lard.

Two weeks later, on Mother's Day, Grandmother Carrie dressed the girls in white: underwear, shoes, socks and ribbons. Snipping two of her biggest Butterfly white roses, she pinned them on their dresses at the top of their Peter Pan collars. When Laurel walked into Sunday school, a girl in her class blurted out. "Oh, look!" She pointed her finger at Laurel. "She's wearing a white flower."

Laurel slumped down in her seat, wishing her mother were alive so she could wear Royalty red like the other children—or even Perfection pink that looked like cotton candy—which would mean her mother was sick. She looked around and saw that Valle and she were the only ones wearing white roses.

After Sunday school that same girl—her braids swinging behind—rushed up to Laurel. "You don't have a mommy? How did she die? Did you cry? Do you miss her? Is your daddy your mommy?"

Laurel thought about the stories she had heard and started to make up her own. Her lips quivered. No words came. Instead something inside of her crumbled—like the hardened glue from the spine of her mother's album. She wanted to slip into a dark hole like water down a drain. What kind of mother would die and leave her baby, she wondered.

"You look a mess," Valle said, coming over to Laurel, reaching up to catch a tear rolling over her lips.

"That little girl said I didn't have a mommy."

"Don't be a baby," scolded Valle. "Stop crying and wipe your eyes." She pulled Laurel into the rest room. "The next time somebody asks you, just look them dead in the eye and say she died from natural causes."

Laurel splashed her face with water. "What's 'natural causes'?"

"Don't you know anything, dum bun?" Valle sounded exasperated. "It's something you say so they don't ask you any more."

"Oh," Laurel said. "Well, what causes it to be natural?"

"Anything that happens naturally is natural. Don't you know that?"

Laurel said nothing. She wanted to figure this out for herself. With an air of authority and her nose upturned, Laurel marched back to the parish hall, looked straight into the questioning girl's eye and said, "Natural Causes," as though everybody would knew what that meant and if they didn't, wouldn't dare ask.

"Oh, yeah, I know," the girl muttered. "My uncle died from that." She turned and walked away.

"Natural Causes" seemed to satisfy the girl with swinging braids. And Laurel decided it was enough of an answer for herself, too. She never again asked Grandmother Carrie why the angels had taken her mother away.

Dance with Me

(To my friend Cleveland Pennington)

A smile
propped up
by broken promises
saddens the heart

Loneliness
hovers vulture-like
threatening to extinguish
his faint inner light

Gone are the Hollywood
contacts
the Las Vegas neon nights
the Lake Tahoe grandeur
Gone, the television specials
limousines
late night suppers
and secret rendezvous
Gone, the gay friends
and associates
saddest of all
the abandonment
by the captain
of his heart
his mother

Now
at every opportunity
Pioneering specialists
poke and prick his vanishing flesh
increasing the already
deadly pain
making his journey
over Jordon
all the more desirable

Ash-gray skin
Pinto insignia
buddy-brown
to black

Dry cornstalk frame
lamenting
at every stirring
of the summer breeze

Fingers
like dry river beds
reach out
for quenching relief

Suppleness, softness
radiance
an inner glow
have long since fled

Blood-red
window panes
emit a faint light
as sparse
strands of straw
lay chemically dead
upon his skull

An exposed skeleton
pokes at material
hanging ghost-like
on pale thin skin
He's in the final stage
of A.I.D.S...

How long
before a strong
winter wind
snaps
the dry
cornstalk frame in two
or vultures
devour the last
flesh of hope
or
an insensitive bureaucracy
sends the pink slip
How long?

My friend and I
sat at a card table
on "Mother's Day"
remembering
April, May and June
Now, I weep in December

Wrong Number

I turned off the water and stepped out of the shower. After toweling off I walked into the bedroom and looked into the mirror. I had lost ten pounds and it really made a difference. My dark brown stomach was smooth and flat again. My hair was long, strong and healthy thanks to my new beautician. Yes, I was pleased with myself. I stepped away from the mirror and looked into my drawer for a nightshirt to put on. I pulled out an oversized T-shirt, then changed my mind and grabbed my satin nightgown. I put on the gown, gave my hair a few strokes with the brush then put it into a ponytail. I looked at the clock, it was 10:15 p.m. I picked up the paperback novel I'd been reading then got into bed. I had read only three pages when the telephone rang:

"Hello" I said

"Hello, may I speak to Henry?" a male voice said.

"I'm sorry, you have the wrong number," I said

"Oh, I'm sorry, is this..."

"I'm sorry you have the wrong number," I said cutting him off.

" I'm very sorry sweet lady don't get upset."

"I'm not upset. I just hate wrong numbers."

"Well I'm very sorry to have disturbed such a beautiful woman as you."

I laughed. "Now how do you know I'm beautiful?"

"I have one of those video phones." We both laughed.

He had such a nice voice: soft, deep and sensuous. I found myself relaxing and tossing my novel to the side.

"No really, I can tell you are beautiful, by your voice and the way you pronounce your words."

"Oh, so what else can you tell about me?"

"I can tell that you are intelligent, sexy, a luscious Nubian Goddess and a great kisser," he continued on, his voice getting deeper and sexier.

I laughed hard then replied, "Go on."

"I can tell that you're the type of woman that needs a lot of love."

"Really," I said still smiling.

"What is your name?" he said coming out of his sexy voice momentarily.

"You mean you can't tell that by the way I talk?" I laughed again. For some reason I was really enjoying the conversation.

He laughed a very slow sexy laugh. Chills suddenly went up and down my spine.

"I think I'll call you Lacy."

"Lacy! Why Lacy?" I shouted.

"Because I bet you have on something soft and lacy."

I couldn't stop giggling.

"So tell me Lacy. Are you happy?" he asked back, in his sexy voice.

"I suppose so. What about you, are you happy Mr. Sexy?"

"Mr. Sexy!" he said. "OK you can call me that for now. So tell me what makes you happy?"

"Wait, you didn't answer me yet," I demanded softly.

"Well I would be happier if I were there with you," he replied.

"So what would you be doing if you were here?" I asked daringly.

He let out a soft moan. There was a long pause. Then he said:

"Well first I would kiss you on your forehead, then your cheeks, then your soft sweet lips. Then I would caress your shoulders and kiss them gently. Next I would softly kiss your neck front, back and side."

I continued to smile shamelessly as he continued.

"I would slowly lower the straps on your soft and lacy gown until it fell to the floor."

I sat up and squirmed a little. He continued." I would caress your body from head to toe and put a kiss everywhere I touch. I would start with your luscious breasts taking them one at a time then together." He paused for a moment then started again. "I would kiss you from front to back, from head to toe around to your navel."

I burst out with laughter. He began to laugh too.

"I see you like the Whispers, huh!" I said.

"Yeah, I like them, but I just said that to see if you were listening."

"Oh, I'm listening. So what else would you do?"

"After that, I would gently spread your legs and I would bury my face."

Suddenly there was a click on the line. He paused.

"Do you have another call?"

"Yeah I guess, but I won't answer it. Go on I want to hear this."

"Yeah, okay I would put my tongue..."

There was another click.

"Shit," I said.

"Maybe you better get that. I don't like to rush these type of things."

I smiled then said, "Alright, let me get it then. I'll be right back. Just remember where you were."

"Hello," I said. There was no answer. "Hello." I said again. Then I heard a click.

I clicked the line and said hello again.

"Hello," I heard my sister say.

"Pam, what are you doing calling so late?"

"Oh, I didn't want anything. I just couldn't sleep."

"Hold on a minute. I have a call on the other line."

I pressed the button to get back to Mr. Sexy. "Hello, Hello," I said. But there was no answer.

"Hello," I said again.

"I'm here," my sister Pam said. Then I realized he was gone.

"Who were you talking to anyway?" she asked.

"Oh it was just a wrong number," I said disappointedly.

The Day the Tears Stopped

It was August 30, 1967. She stood over him and listened to the rattle in his chest. She had heard the words "death rattle" before and assumed it was just something said. The concept was so strange, it couldn't possibly have been true. But, there it was, clear, unmistakable and unceasing. He lay very still on the twin-size bed, no movement except the uneven heaving of his chest; the sound reverberated through the small room. She stood silently for what seemed like a very long time, but may have been only a few minutes. She examined him from head to toe and reflected on her own fear of facing his mortality. He was her father and their relationship had never been good.

Years later she would reflect back on the fact that he never touched her other than to hit. She could not recall that he ever hugged or kissed, patted or showed her any sign of physical affection. Though she could remember back to age three, she had no memories of affection from him. He was not a cruel man, just undemonstrative. In this, which turned out to be his final year, they had worked out a truce, of sorts. She had wanted so much more than he could or would give her. In that last year, she had given up, or more accurately tried to give up the anger and resentment she felt for what she perceived to be his failure to provide for her financially and emotionally. She was, after all, a graduating senior and she had made it through college mostly without his help.

In that final year, they could actually sit and talk, watch television together, run errands together as his illness progressed. She drove him to the market, to doctor's appointments and for other things he needed. She saw him for what he was, a man who had done his best. His illness had slowed his step and stooped his back, he looked old beyond his years. He was 63. His health had failed him and he was facing his own mortality. Her anger was a burden she didn't need and didn't have energy or room for in her life. It was so unfair. After all, they were making peace with each other, she was giving up her anger toward him and now he was going away. She had wanted so much more.

The rattle continued until she couldn't listen any longer. She walked out past her family and a few visitors. It was a typical Oklahoma August day. The sun beat down and reflected off the asphalt streets. The waves of heat bounced up to greet her. She walked slowly, it was a different kind of day and she was different today. The hurried way she usually walked was out of place. She was aware of the heat, but unaware of the slowness of her pace. She was hoping to temporarily escape from the inevitable events taking place at her house. Silently, she walked down the street and to her friend's grandmother's house. She had always liked her and called her grandmother. She sat and talked with her for about an hour and one-half. They talked about so many things but she could not bring herself to tell her why she had come. The pain was too great. When grandmother asked her about her father, she said he wasn't doing very well and nothing more. It was a time, a brief time to step outside the pain and not deal with it. She had no idea how she was going to handle it.

It was time for her to go back. She walked back in the blazing sun, dreading the death rattle and the finality of what would face her when she returned. As she stepped into the small house, it greeted her at the door. She said nothing to those in the house, she simply walked straight back into the room as if the rattle were beckoning her. Minutes passed and the rattle became louder and more uneven.

Her mother came into the room, sat down beside him, rubbed his forehead and held his hand for a brief time. He seemed to respond, a little. She then got up and walked out of the room. Others were walking in and out of the room, but she wouldn't...couldn't leave. A member of their church, with no sense of their need for privacy, came into the room and refused to leave. She felt anger, extreme anger, but she couldn't deal with her. Then it was there, the final breath. It wasn't labored, like she expected, just quietly, his breathing stopped. The silence stunned her and seemed to fill up the small room. She felt so heavy, her heart seemed as heavy as the silence in the room. She had to tell her mother, who was busying herself in the kitchen. As she started out of the room, her mother appeared in the hallway. She told her he was dead.

Her mother dropped her head, but didn't say a word, then she walked back into the living room. She had to tell her sister, she was only 13, Daddy's baby. She called her brother. She called her other brother. She called her older sister who lived in another city. She and her younger sister walked outside and sat on the porch, she cried a little, but not much. Her sister sobbed loudly and she held her. As they rocked back and forth, she concentrated on pulling herself together. Tears would not be of much help to her. The postman asked what the problem was, she drew herself together to say that her father had just died. She struggled with her need not to cry. She couldn't let herself cry. The pain was too great, all those years of distance and dissension. She couldn't have those years back. She wouldn't cry today. Just like the book she had read several years earlier she told herself, "I'll cry tomorrow. I'll cry when I can be in control. I'll cry when I can be sure

I'll be able to stop. I'll cry later when the pain isn't so terrible. I'll cry when I can handle it."

Before the hearse came, she and her mother stripped the beds and removed his clothes. Her mother walked out of the room. She stood beside the bed and stared at his naked body. How strange it was to see him there. He was alive a few minutes before; now he lay in final silence. She stared at him intently, observing the marked contrast between the paleness of his chest, legs and arms and the bronze of his face, neck and hands. She observed his genitals and thought of the fact that she and all her brothers and sisters had come from there. She also reflected on the fact that at any other time it would have been so inappropriate to observe him in his nakedness. She stood very still and stared until her mother returned. They covered his body with a clean sheet. She still didn't leave the room; she sat on the edge of the bed and waited for she wasn't sure what.

After the hearse came, her mother said they had to go to the laundromat. They gathered up the bedclothes and sheets and went to the laundry. It was her mother's way of starting to deal with the reality of the loss of her husband of 30 years. They didn't talk except about the laundry. It was a short ride and silent task. She and her mother were talkers, but today there was nothing to say, or maybe there was too much to say. They never talked about the death of her father, not that day or any day after that. They went back to the house, there were more people there. The people kept coming until late into the night.

She had pulled herself together. She thought she was doing O.K. until she lay her body down to sleep. She was in the room where he died. She was to sleep in the twin bed next to the one where he drew his last breath. The need to cry overwhelmed her. Her eyes filled up with tears and her body was wracked with the pain of it all. She would not give into it. There was no need, after all. She held herself tightly and fought back the tears. The night passed slowly, the need to cry came in deep waves that almost seemed to overwhelm her. Wave after wave she fought them back. She held on to herself tightly and rocked and rocked. She would not cry, after all the tears might never stop. How could she let them flow when she might not be able to stop them. She wrapped her arms around her body and rocked herself off and on all night. Sleep came intermittently, that night and for many nights after that.

He died registration week of her senior year. The funeral was a struggle. When she awakened in the morning the August sky was black with big billowy clouds. They seemed to hang very low in the sky and the rains came in torrents. The darkness closed in on her and the rain poured down on her like the waves of pain from the night before. She felt so heavy, so slow, so overwhelmed. She sat silently amongst her family during the funeral and listened to the sounds of grief. Later, she sat with them in the limousine and listened to them cry aloud. The tears fell but she remained silent. Her mother turned to them and told them: "At least he isn't suffering any more."

It was time to go back to school. Usually, he drove her to school, it had been his small contribution after paying for her freshman year. After three weeks she went home for the weekend. She went through the motions of pretending things weren't that different. That night, when she lay down to sleep, she slept in the bed where he died. The waves came back with a vengeance. She had told herself she would be O.K. She was surprised at the strength of the waves but she would not cry. It was too soon, the pain was too new, too raw. Later, much later, she told herself, she would give herself permission to cry.

Nearly two years later her brother died. He was only 30. He had led the short troubled life of an alcoholic. At his funeral she stood over the casket and stared down at the almost unrecognizable figure. In life her brother had beautiful ebony skin and jet black curly hair. What she saw in that casket was someone with gray, clay like skin and he was wearing glasses. She asked herself, "Why is he wearing glasses, he almost never wore them?" She stood and stared and her legs gave way, she could no longer stand. Her husband picked her limp body up and carried her to the car. She never cried and they didn't talk about how horrible it all was. They never talked about it at all. She was married to a man who had no understanding or sympathy for tears. So, the tears didn't come. Who would comfort her if she cried? She remembered what to do this time. Hold on, hold on, rock, rock, rock, "This too shall pass."

Years passed, a troubled marriage, divorce, friends lost through distance and death but the tears were gone. She lived with the heartbreak of broken promises from her husband, beginning with their marriage vows and including a long string of infidelities. Added to that were the normal disappointments of life, but the tears were gone. With the passage of time they got further away.

She had taught herself not to cry and now she wanted so badly to teach herself to let go. How she envied the free tears of others at movies, weddings, funerals and other appropriate or even not so appropriate occasions. She often looks for them, waits for them, longs for them. But, they just will not come.

Death on Del Monte

(For Michael James Bryant, d. 1993)

On Del Monte
peach blossoms drop from trees,
    Jacaranda leaves
carpet walks
    evening falls
    like a stroke

as hickory smoke drifts
from the corner where
dark hands fill plates;
food
for friends and family
who have come to pay their
last respects to a barber.

Bryant was his name.
In front of the barber shop
where he cut hair,
candles flicker
in his memory.

To his neighbors
he was a father, a son,
a barber who gave free haircuts
to the poor
but the police didn't care who he was
when they chased him down,
    tased him,
        hog-tied him. To them
he was just another
    nigger.

On Del Monte
shadows fall silently
like footsteps leaving;
the Moon sheds
    silver
       tears.

Uncle Cal

Uncle Cal lived ten miles down the road from Hattie Mae. She had never been to his house, but had seen him many times heading down the road toward town; his figure tall, dark, and bent like an old fig tree. Whenever she saw him, she hid behind the house and watched him go by. She could never figure out what it was about him that frightened her. Perhaps it was the way his head bent forward, bobbing up and down in rhythm with the horses. Or the way his coat tails flapped like the wings of a giant bird. Or perhaps it was the stories she heard about him.

Stories about Uncle Cal spread throughout Hopeful, Georgia like love bugs in summer. Some said he had magical powers and could cure diseases with roots and herbs. Some said he had once raised a man from the dead. Supposedly, old Sam had been shot by the sheriff for stealing watermelons from Mr. Carter's plantation. The sheriff had called his wife to come pick up his body. In desperation, she had taken his body to Uncle Cal's. Lo and behold, Sam was seen sitting beside his wife in their buggy the next day.

Hattie Mae wasn't sure if she believed any of the stories about Uncle Cal, but she knew there was something strange about him. She was determined to keep her distance from him until she met Jake Wesley that is.

She had never known a man like Jake before. He had lived up North in New York for the last eight years and had come home to live with his Aunt Jessie. Some say he was hiding from the law, but Hattie Mae ignored the gossip.

She met him on one of her trips into town to buy supplies. "Ooo wee," he said, as she stepped out of the General Store. "If you ain't the prettiest thing South of the Mason Dixie line, I'll be a coon's ass."

His sudden outburst had caused a blush to creep up the sides of her face. She dropped her head in embarrassment and almost tripped down the steps as she headed toward her wagon. She tried to ignore him, but he fell into step behind her.

"Say, Miss, whas yo' name? Can I have the pleasure of buying you a soda?"

She blushed again and began loading her goods into the wagon.

"Here let me help you," he said, stepping forward and taking a twenty pound sack of flour from her arms. Just then Big John, Hattie

Mae's grandfather, showed up. He shot Jake a venomous look and ordered Hattie Mae into the wagon. Then he loaded the rest of the goods onto the wagon and took off without saying another word.

All over town, Big John was known as a quiet man with a temper bad as a tornado. Even the sheriff cut a wide path around him.

All the way home, Hattie Mae could not get Jake out of her mind. Perhaps it was the way he wore his hair slicked back with pomade. Or was it the smooth, honey brown, texture of his skin? Or the even whiteness of his teeth? Whatever it was, it had taken hold of her like a honeysuckle wrapped around a tree and would not let her go.

The next week she jumped at the opportunity to go into town when her grandmother mentioned that they had run out of lye, which she needed for making soap. This time she put on her best dress, the one with big yellow sunflowers all over. And she wore a big wide-brimmed straw hat instead of the hanky she usually tied around her head.

Sure enough, Jake was leaning against a pole in front of the General Store.

"Good afternoon, Miss," he said as she walked past him. "I been coming here every day since last week, hoping I would run into you. I sure would likes to get to know you better. Would you mind if I came a callin' on you some evening?"

Hattie Mae's tongue tied into a knot. So far the only boy who had ever come calling on her was Willie Boy, who was short and ugly with buck teeth. None of the girls at church liked him. Sometimes Hattie Mae felt sorry for him, and would sit on the porch steps with him, but she always kept her distance. Once he had tried to kiss her when Big John was not looking. She had jumped up and run into the house, refusing to come out no matter how hard he begged.

But she knew that since she had just turned fifteen, Big John would never approve of her seeing Jake. Every since her Mama had run off with a smooth city man right after she was born, Big John had distrusted all men. He refused to let any boy but Willie Boy come near her. And the only reason he let him come by was because he knew she did not like him.

Hattie Mae explained that Big John would never consent to his coming to call on her, but she offered to meet him down the road. Even she was surprised at her boldness, offering to meet a stranger on a lonesome road. After she finished her shopping, she hurried down the road. Sure enough, she had barely gone a mile, when she spotted him sitting under a tree. She parked the wagon along side the road and he helped her climb down from it. They walked down the hill a bit and talked. He told her that he had moved to Hopeful to help his Aunt

Jessie on the farm. Soon they were laughing and talking like old friends. Hattie Mae was fascinated by the stories he told. He talked about places in Harlem with fancy names like Lenox Avenue and Sugar Hill. He was the most worldly man she had every known, not to mention the most handsome. That afternoon they spent a short time together, but agreed to meet again the next week. Soon they were meeting once a week.

One day he asked her to meet him late that evening near Coon's Creek. Hattie Mae agreed only after he promised that he would not keep her out long. He said he had something important to tell her.

That night while Miss Pearl and Big John snored loudly, Hattie Mae tiptoed out of the house and ran down to the creek. Sure enough Jake was waiting there for her. He looked even more handsome, his face aglow in the moonlight. "I want you to be my wife," he said, when they had settled on the ground under a Sweet gum tree.

"But what about all those pretty ladies in Harlem?" Hattie Mae teased.

"What ladies?" The look on his face turned serious. His eyes caressed her face. Suddenly he leaned forward and scooped her in his arms.

Swept away by the moonlight, the warmth of his arms encircling her, the smell of his body, she weakened. Before she knew it, she was lying on the ground and he was on top of her. Somewhere in the distance a frog croaked. A dog howled. Crickets played a symphony. The wind tickled the leaves.

That night Hattie Mae crept back into the house and crawled into bed. She was under his spell now more than ever.

After that night there were many clandestine trips to Coon's Creek. Then one morning when Miss Pearl was fixing grits, eggs and fatback for breakfast, Hattie Mae bolted from the table and ran outside. She could not stand the smell of the fatback frying in the pan. She barely made it outside before she threw up. She was hanging over the side rail when Miss Pearl came outside.

"What's wrong with you gal?" Miss Pearl demanded.

"I don't know Mother Pearl. I just felt poorly all of a sudden. I must have a touch of the flu."

Miss Pearl's eyes bore a hole in Hattie Mae's. "You ain't been messin' with that new fella I heared about?"

"Naw Mother Pearl, what make you think somethin' like that?" Hattie Mae's eyes grew big and round.

"Don't lie to me gal." Miss Pearl's hand shot out and slapped Hattie Mae across the face. "I knows when a gal's in a family way. I just hope and pray that Big John don't find out."

The words had barely come out of Miss Pearl's mouth when Big John appeared in the doorway.

"Hope I don't find out what?" he demanded. He looked first at Miss Pearl's face and then Hattie Mae's stricken face. Then a storm brewed in his eyes.

"That no good dog," he said, "I'll kill him." Without uttering another word, he turned, and went into the back room. When he returned he was carrying his double barrel shotgun.

Everyone knew Big John was a man of few words and quick action. So Hattie Mae and Miss Pearl knew he meant it when he said he'd kill Jake.

"Now Big John, put that gun down befo' you do something foolish." Miss Pearl stood in his way.

With one arm, he brushed her aside and strode toward the barn. Hattie Mae ran after him, pleading and crying. But he ignored her and kept on walking. He hitched the horse to his wagon and took off down the road like he was chasing the devil himself.

Hattie Mae stood in the middle of the road, stricken with hurt and grief. Then suddenly she knew she had to warn Jake. The wagon Big John used to take Hattie and Miss Pearl to church was sitting on the side of the barn. In no time Hattie Mae had it hitched to Fanny, the old mare they used to plow the fields, and took off after Big John.

She knew just where to find Jake. He usually spent his afternoons sitting in front of Pete's Corner Store chewing the fat with the Jackson boys. She got there just after Big John rounded the corner. When the boys saw Big John coming at them with his shotgun raised, they scattered like crows being chased out of a corn field. But Jake, who had been sitting on a stool near the door did not move fast enough. The last thing he heard was the explosion from Big John's shotgun.

The next thing anybody knew, he was lying in the middle of the road, a hole big as a fifty cent piece in his chest. Hattie Mae screamed and ran to him. Big John tried to stop her but she tore loose from him and knelt beside him. No one doubted that he was dead. His eyes had rolled to the back of his head and blood poured from the gaping hole in his chest. There was nothing left to do but take him to Old Man Davis' funeral parlor.

When Big John left, the boys lifted Jake's body and was about to place him on a wagon that stood on the side of the road. But before they could place his body on the wagon, Hattie Mae screamed, "No, Put him in my wagon. I'll take care of him."

The men looked sheepishly at each other. No one said a word. They then placed his body in Hattie's wagon and watched as she drove off toward the funeral home.

Hattie Mae was half way down the road when she struck upon an idea. She remembered the stories about Uncle Cal. What if he could help Jake? The idea terrified and compelled her at the same time. When she came to the fork in the road, she took the road that led to Uncle Cal's house.

Uncle Cal's house stood in the middle of a thick underbrush about fifteen miles outside of town. The sun had begun to set when Hattie Mae pulled her wagon up to his gate and stepped down from it. At first she thought he wasn't home, but when she knocked on the door she heard footsteps inside.

"Who is it?" a voice answered from inside the house.

"It's Hattie Mae, Miss Pearl's granddaughter," she said.

The door opened and Uncle Cal stood in the doorway. He was smaller than Hattie Mae imagined with skin that looked like the bark of an old pine tree and patches of gray hair on both sides of his head.

He peered at her suspiciously. "What you doin' out here this time a evening. I spect this ain't no social visit," he muttered.

"No Suh." Hattie Mae tried to hold back the tears that welled in her eyes, "I heard you could heal folks. I thought maybe you could help Jake. He's been shot." She pointed toward the wagon.

Uncle Cal's eyes followed her finger. He didn't say anything. Then he stepped outside and went over to the wagon. He stood there looking at Jake's body for a moment and then he came back to the porch.

"That man's dead as a log," he said, shaking his head. "Tain't nothin' I kin do for him."

"But I heard you had special powers. I heard you could save him."

Uncle Cal's eyes narrowed. "Chile can't nobody raise the dead but the Lord Jesus. And Jesus I ain't. Now if you'll excuse me I was about to fix muh supper."

He headed inside the house but Hattie Mae grabbed his arm.

"Uncle Cal please!" she said, "I'm expecting his baby. If you don't save him, my baby won't have no daddy."

Uncle Cal stopped, turned, and scratched his head. He considered what she said for a moment.

"I ain't promising no miracles," he finally said, "but I'll see what I kin do."

Together they lifted Jake's body off the wagon and carried him into the house. They laid him on a cot in the back room. Then Uncle Cal told Hattie Mae to wait in the front room.

Hattie Mae watched as Uncle Cal performed his magic. He moved slowly from the kitchen to the back room. In the kitchen he boiled a large pot of water. To the water he added different ingredients from some jars he kept in the cupboard. He then took the pot in the back room.

As Hattie Mae sat in the front room, she could hear him speaking in a strange tongue. A few hours later, he emerged through the curtain which hung over the doorway.

"You kin go in and see him now," he said. "But remember he's weak from losing so much blood."

Hattie Mae rushed between the curtains separating the rooms and found Jake lying on the bed, his chest covered with a thick bandage.

"Jake," she whispered. "Can you hear me?"

She almost passed out when his hand reached out and touched hers. Then his eyes opened.

"Is that you Baby?" he asked.

Hattie Mae could not believe her ears. Jake was alive. She offered to come to work for Uncle Cal to pay him for bringing Jake back to life but he refused, saying that she should just bring the baby round to see him when it was born.

The moon was full when Hattie Mae helped Jake climb on the wagon and they both waved good-bye to Uncle Cal.

The next day one of the Jackson boys swore he saw Jake sitting next to Hattie Mae in the buggy big as day. But they disappeared and were never seen nor heard from again. Some say they took the train to New York and are living in Harlem. Still others say they see them from time to time when the moon is full, lying by the creek or they hear the creaking wheels of the wagon and the hoofs of the old mare trotting down the road.

Powerful

From the window of her four-story walkup, Elaine looked for signs of Lance, hoping to catch him trudging through the snow. It was after seven on a Monday night and he should've been home by now. She knew where he was supposed to be coming from. With spring a month away, he started an intermediate swimming program at the "Y." He liked to go on late afternoons while the masses would be at work; that way, he'd have the pool mostly to himself. And no matter how late he might have left for the Y, and no matter how hard Elaine tried, he was always gone by the time she came home from work.

They first met several months ago when he had just moved back to Chicago after living in New York for five years. He had moved there after graduating from college. In search of a music career as a studio musician, he fled the "boring" life of the Midwestern suburbs, supporting himself as a computer programmer during the day and chasing his artistic dreams at night. After two years on the job as a programmer, he got fired for not taking his job seriously enough. Before having to move back home to his parents, however, he was able to make a recording with a band from New Jersey. He brought the album back with him, a souvenir. He mounted it in his parent's living room next to the plaque he won in high school for chemistry. It now sat in her apartment on the mantle of the non-working fireplace. Looking at it now, it makes her envious, evidence of the life he's lived without her.

Lance started his swimming routine to complement the joint workouts they used to do at home together. Not that stretching and lifting weights together weren't great, he told her, but he wanted to swim, too. She could swim a little, but nothing like the laps he boasted of doing. One lap was enough for her; besides, the only thing she wanted to do with consistency these days was to keep her mind from wandering. There was a time not long ago when, lying in bed together, arms and legs intertwined, she could convince herself for the hundredth time how silly she was to ever be insecure. But that was when he was touching her. All she thought about for the moment was how late he was for dinner. That, coupled with the smell of vegetarian lasagna in the oven, irritated her even more, tantamount to suffocation. It's spicy scent conjured up the image of her stopping by the Peacock fruit stand, after work and on a mission, squeezing the tomatoes and sniffing green peppers for freshness, the way he taught her;

that, and suffering a sting from the onion juice that seeped into a cut on her finger. He said he preferred his onions sliced thin; she cut her finger trying to make the slices as thin as possible, an expression of love without the words. And here he had her standing by the window, waiting.

Ever since she saw him with that other woman she began to worry. It was while they were shopping for vintage clothes, a store he discovered in her neighborhood. As she was helping him try on sports coats, he suggested she might want to look at the hand-made baskets against the wall They were on the other side of the store. He told her it'd be neat to have a picnic basket for carrying cucumber sandwiches and fruit to the beach the following summer. She left to investigate, just as he suggested, without a care in the world. A second thought about dress ties for him caused her to turn around and start to shout something. But her voice failed her when she saw, from a distance, that Lance had moved away from the sports coat section. She stood frozen and watched as he slowly approached a woman trying on hats. He stood inches from her as he slowly removed his flannel shirt and his t-shirt without taking his eyes off the woman. His right nipple was a mere tongue extension from her mouth! When she saw him mouth words to her and she responded with a smile, that was when things changed. Others were capable of loving him; she hadn't considered that. The thought scared her, like a brush with death. She knew then and there she could never, would never, confront him with what she had witnessed.

Lance introduced her to his vintage-clothes-buying routine as a way of saving money on her receptionist's salary. That, and the joy of sharing time together, is something he wanted when he first moved in with her. At first she was timid, feeling that buying used clothing was beneath her. Then she began to enjoy it with abandon. But after the incident in the store, she grew afraid of shopping in big, open spaces with him, where they might browse independently. That was just asking for trouble. Now she could never let him out of her sight without feeling anxious.

She didn't want to harp on this just now, though. Lance might come through the door any minutes and dinner would be served. Maybe this time it would be like the way things used to be, the days when she read while he practiced on his keyboards. After that, they would bend, stretch and lift weights in the bedroom, collapse on top of each other like wet clay. Eventually they would shower and then make love on the mattress placed in front of the fireplace. That's because her cheap wooden bed frame, which she bought a year ago, cracked under the strain of their lovemaking. Besides, her bedroom was now the weight room. She recalled how they laughed in triumph as they broke the old bed frame into pieces narrow enough to slide down the garage chute off her back porch. Things grew more passionate after that, uninhibited by a cheap bed frame or four bedroom walls.

She holds on to these thoughts as she enters her old bedroom which is now the gym. The black padded weight bench with its steel gray frame holds a stack of his t-shirts, folded. Next to them is a second pair of swim trunks he owns and his hair brush. She picks it up and inspects it closely. There are strands of his hair, in the shape of 9's, wrapped around mylon bristles. She puts the brush to her nose and sniffs. Inhaling his scent deeply, she forgets briefly about his being late, the lasagna in the oven, or even the cut on her finger. She holds him in her hand for a moment, just like that, validating objects in the room as evidence he is very much in her life—the weight bench, his folded t-shirts, a closet full of his clothes and his favorite pair of wingtips, parked like cars in the closet. With the brush against her nose she reasons how silly she has been. Hadn't he always wanted to be here? There was proof. He was still moving things in from his parents' house—the spare halogen lamp from his father's desk, the threadbare laundry rug his mother wouldn't miss. She had met his parents once, albeit under disastrous circumstances, but they knew she existed. They knew he was living with her. They were her witnesses.

That was the time Lance talked her into turning a two-day weekend into a three-day one spending it at his parent's house. They owned a four-bedroom home in an affluent suburb. His parents were both out of town, he told her, and they'd have the house to themselves—the rear-projection TV and the well-stocked refrigerator. His father, a chemist, was in Cincinnati at a conference; his mother was spending time in the city with a sister. She took up his offer eagerly, glad to get away from her tiny apartment. They spent the whole weekend watching video movies and looking at family album photos. She felt family pictures might bring them closer. She even pressed her lips to a picture of him in his high school senior portrait, while he waited for her in bed upstairs. It was nailed on the wall opposite the staircase, along with the rest of his sisters, spaced properly and in ascending order.

This happened while on her way to the kitchen for two glasses of orange juice. The white European-styled cabinets had Mason jars filled with pasta in the shape of sea shells, rainbow colors, mixed nuts and dried beans on the top shelf. On the bottom shelf were packages of cookies with European names, some she was familiar with and some she was not. On the top shelf of another cabinet were tins of different teas, some with Chinese writing. On a shelf below that were coffee mugs which were black on the outside, turquoise, pink or blue on the inside. She briefly lost sight of her mission for glasses when she became frustrated by an expresso machine and a coffee grinder on the kitchen counter. They both looked as though they had just come off a store shelf, spotless. By the time she got to the last cabinet she found what she was looking for. On the bottom shelf of that cabinet were glasses which looked suitable for orange juice.

With a glass in each hand she turned slowly in a circle, as though she were a light house, fantasizing how nice it would be if that were her kitchen. She would never have minded cooking for Lance in that room, she told herself, with its white-tiled counters, dual stainless steel sink and six-burner stove, its German grand name written in austere lettering, flanked by huge knobs on either side. She would even have put her knees on that floor in order to clean it, the way her mother did as a young girl. She couldn't imagine what Lance saw in her apartment. It reminded her of the cavity in progression on her back tooth, accessible only by a landing of creaky stairs, draped in carpet that is filthy and holds the odors of human transiency. She never wanted to go back there.

By the time Sunday night rolled around she found she couldn't sleep, knowing that they had to go back to her world the next day. Going back alone would upset her even more. She kept thoughts like those and others close to her chest. He told her he couldn't wait to get back to the city, get out of his parents house. She wasn't sure she believed him. Maybe he felt guilty, having watched her reaction as she took in his parents' wealth. She made plans to suggest they get a better apartment once he started working.

She woke up at six the next morning and stared down at his face which was cloaked in shadows. She kissed its little-boy expression, placed it in her mind and brought it downstairs with her. Wrapped in his blue and white checkered robe, she planned to cook him a breakfast in that beautiful white and stainless steel kitchen. As she was stirring the pancake batter with a wooden spoon, she thought she heard him moving about. Wanting to be caught in the act of industry, she stirred more vigorously. She lovingly laid strips of bacon across the face of a cast iron skillet. As she turned toward the refrigerator to return the bacon, she locked eyes with a woman she knew was his mother, standing in the doorway, watching. She was standing there in a thick coat, the color of sand, holding her purse against her chest. as though for protection. All Elaine could think about was her hair, never mind the fact that she was a stranger in another woman's kitchen. Her lips moved but she couldn't hear her own voice. She thought she may have said something appropriate, for his mother responded with a thin smile before silently walking away.

To make matters worse, the left front tire of Lance's car, which was parked in front of the house, had a flat. Now he had to change the tire before they could leave, allowing his mother to observe them from the picture window, disgusted no doubt at finding this trespasser playing house in her kitchen. Before Lance had a chance to finish changing the tire, his father pulled up in a black limousine. He paid the chauffeur as he watched his son give the crowbar one final turn. Rather than say hello, the father pulled his garment bag over his shoulder while shoving his wallet in his breast pocket. Elaine said hello but he ignored her. Out of ear shot, Lance muttered to her that he probably hadn't heard her.

Placing Lance's hair brush down on the weight bench brings her back to now, thoughts of baskets filled with cucumber sandwiches, and betrayal. She checks once again on the lasagna. The sauce is congealing as the recipe said it would. That's good. She's in the market for certainty tonight and recipes are a start. The four black burners on the stove, especially the two in the back, remind her of feelings she's tried to defer. She has never been able to do that, place her feelings on the back burner, the way the strong do. That's only a parable from her grandparents and old people like them whose lives could never be this complicated, she tells herself. Like a claim ticket, she holds on to the way things used to be, how at first he really didn't mean that much to her.

She first met him while waiting for a bus at Michigan and Randolph Streets right after work. After some small talk initiated by him, he insisted he had been watching her for weeks on this same corner before he had the courage to walk up and say hello. She blushed when he told her that about his needing days to build up the courage just to speak. Imagine! No man had ever told her that. It was all so sweet, like in a novel. He asked her to meet him for lunch the next day at the Art Institute. She accepted because he seemed safe, they would be going during the daytime, and she was impressed at his meeting place of choice. She learned a lot about Van Gogh that afternoon, and the tragedy of the painter's life touched her. He bought her a post card of Van Gogh's Cornfield With Crows as a thank you for her company. She placed it in a DAX frame on her desk at work. The following Saturday afternoon he called unexpectedly, saying he was just down the street and would she join him for a foreign film and a "veggie" burger. A week later, on her birthday, he bought her a hand-painted bowl, a glass vase and a vegetarian cookbook. There was something very delicate, gentle and kid-like the way he sat cross-legged in his black jeans, wanting her to guess what was inside each neatly wrapped package he set about her living room like large pieces of confetti.

The first time he kissed her he held her face in his hands. The newness of kissing him for the first time, the delicate touch of his long fingers on her face, made her lose her breath. The next night they spent the evening facing each other in her bathrobe. The only light came from candles placed strategically on the vanity and the floor. She remembers it like yesterday, facing each other in a warm bubble bath spiced with a handful of his mother's favorite bath beads. She likes to believe it left its smell on her skin for two days. Afterwards, he tamed her nagging headache by rubbing the soles of her feet. That's when she began to let him in her life. That's when she started wanting to see him in her apartment daily. After all, he was the man that waited for her on the bus stop every day. She told him she loved him.

"What do you see in me?" he asked incredulously when she told him that. "I'm so skinny, I have a terrible profile and I don't have a job."

She remembers countering with how terribly handsome he was, patiently building up what he tore down. He had grown on her and she'd gotten used to his body, somehow. It wasn't Michelangelo's David, but she loved it. She could never understand why the world couldn't see it too. But ever since the episode in the vintage clothing store he has become intoxicating. She found herself wanting to be with him all the time, even at the expense of her best friend, Tracey, something she couldn't have imagined in the very beginning. As time passed on, she realized her feelings were obsessive, needing him more. Meanwhile he grew more powerful, more confident and needing her less. Suddenly, he loved his profile. Then she began losing him at parties. By the time of the hand-made basket incident, she rarely found him home when she got there. If he wasn't on a job interview, he was out for fresh air, or so he said. Despite her will, she felt less and less in control. This manifested itself when she couldn't make him understand how she felt. The more she tried, the more unsure she felt about her own feelings, mirrored against his incapacity, or lack of desire, to understand her. His ability to roll over and begin snoring after pouring her heart out made her suffer. She sensed one panel of his personality had the word "cruel" spray-painted in jagged scribe. She'd stare at the ceiling while he dreamed, trying to avoid the cadence of his breathing as though she were ducking blows. Out of his arms, she'd lie awake, traveling through the long, lonely night, alone.

As a way to regain power she has started withholding her affection. She'd given too much too soon, she could see that clearly. Unable to take back her words "I love you," she sees this battle as her only alternative. She doesn't roll on his side of the bed unless he touches her first, the way he used to. She is still waiting for the tide to turn but nothing has happened yet. For the last two weeks she's slept alone, in the same bed, with him. These days they only make love in the dark; and even though this act has maintained its intensity, afterward, they retreat to their respective corners, like boxers. She sits in the dark, wide-eyed, waiting for a hand, even a leg, in search of her own. He hasn't seemed to notice the politics of their sleeping arrangement. Either he is unaware of what is going on, in which case she is living dishonestly, or he is more powerful than she is, able to hold out longer than she can.

She finds herself in the hallway when the oven's timer goes off. She brings her eyes into focus and finds herself staring at his beloved keyboard. She runs to the kitchen to remove the lasagna with dish towels. When one of her fingers accidentally touches the pan, it shocks her more than burns her, like a scolding, and the pan falls from one hand, one end of it falling on the floor of the oven with a thud. Cheese splashes everywhere. Lance opens the door and she can feel the cold winter air behind him.

"Hi, honey," he says as though he were greeting a pet.

"Hi," she says, focusing on the mess as a way of ignoring his existence.

"Smells good, I'm hungry," he yells from the bedroom. The music of metal hangers is heard as he hangs up his coat and scarf.

"That's 'cause it is good," she says with an anger powered by the recollection of how he used to kiss her before removing his coat.

"I'm going to take a shower, get this chlorine off me," he shouts from the bedroom.

"Hurry, dinner's ready." Once she hears the bathroom door close, and the sneeze of the shower, she places the lasagna on the stove, shuts the oven door and waits, totally without an appetite. She goes into the bedroom which has the faint smell of chlorine. She feels relieved. No doubt he went swimming and came straight home. She reaches down and quietly unzips his gym bag. With her wounded finger, she touches his wet trunks, for luck. Satisfied, she heads back towards the kitchen, that same finger pressed against her cheek, consoled, prepared to sleep on his side tonight.

Thanks

The little word Thanks is powerful
    and strong
Thanks to our ancestors for the
    race they have run
For bearing 200 years of slavery,
    discrimination and pain
For their hopes and dreams
    of breaking the chains
Of a life of servitude, illiteracy,
    hatred and fears
For holding on and holding out
    through the bitter years
Thanks to the Civil Rights leaders
    of old
To Frederick Douglass, Harriett
    Tubman & others so bold
To Marcus Garvey who taught us
    that Africa means pride
To A. Phillip Randolph who carried
    our workers on a daring ride

Thanks to Martin Luther King
    who had a marvelous dream
To Malcolm X who dared to speak
    loudly and to esteem
The struggle for Black pride and for
    Black economic growth
Both men are still honored, and their
    words we still quote
Thanks to the old Black mothers
    who worked hard and long
To the old Black fathers who were
    much despised and wronged
To Mary McLeod Bethune who built
    a school with her own hands
To Booker T. Washington whose great work
    and institute still stand

Thanks to the great musicians and
    blues singers of old
To Louis Armstrong whose trumpet
    was melodious with soul
To Bessie Smith who died one night
    on a dark lonely road
To Lady Day who belted out beautiful
    melodies untold

Thanks to the writers who left their
    feelings in print
Who told their stories and left
    us a living monument
Thanks to a little slave girl, Phyllis
    Wheatley, who wrote against the law
To Paul Laurence Dunbar who recorded
    the observations he saw
Of the little Black children
    who suffered in pain
Of the old Black men who
    struggled to be unchained
Thanks to Langston Hughes, the
    Dean of the Poets Black
To Alex Haley who discovered our Roots
    as we looked forward and back
Thanks to Claude McKay who declared
    If we must Die
It will not be like hogs, but with
    pride that we can dignify
To Countee Cullen who cried out
    in a poet's voice
He had to express his thought and fears,
    for he had no other choice

Thanks to Margaret Walker—her
    dirges and jubilees ring
Out as the voices of the young,
    black, poor, and those who are still struggling
To Maya Angelou, a little frustrated
    girl from Arkansas' backyard
Whose experiences as a child left
    her all battered and scarred
Yet she rose from the dust
    to pursue her dreams and hopes
And became a phenomenal woman
    always able to cope
Thanks to Thurgood Marshall
    for fighting the good fight
As he courageously and successfully
    argued for our Equal Rights
And for the many years he served
    on the greatest Court in the land
Where he never wavered from
    his commitment to take a mighty stand
Thanks to our Black ancestors much
    maligned and wronged
But they struggled through the
    years so we could remain forever strong

Yes, the little word "thanks" is
    both powerful and strong
Thanks to our past and present leaders
    for the races they have run.

Homecoming

Plastic souls,
Picket fences,
Painted smiles,
Blue contact lenses

But honey chile—
That congo beat
Raised de spirits
Fired up those feet

Down home soul
Muddy Waters blues
Hollerin' hymns,
Packin' 'em pews

Why white bread chile?
My cornbread's cooked
with so much love
my kitchen shook!

God's got his ways
Songs meant to be
No place like home
Where love is free

Past plastic souls
them picket fences
past those painted smiles
'n blue contact lenses.

After the Shackles Are Removed

You bypassed a janitor
leaving your cushy corporate post
uniformed in your monkey suit
    and you didn't return his nod
glanced quickly away
because the piercing blue eyes in the office
were watching.

you ignored my subtle moves, teasing play
and finally blatant passes—
opted for the six o'clock news
flashbacks, visions...Mayor Berry/Clarence
Thomas/Mike Tyson/Rodney King
switched to "Jeopardy"
and split your attention between
"Government Officials"
and my collards, butter beans, and cornbread.

It's nightfall—
the remote control, WALL STREET, and dishes
are put away.
Now I gently remove your shackles
slip off your binding chains
knead your feet
    every callous
tongue your lobe
stroke you into
    my greatest fantasy...

frenzied/carefree/convulsive
love
with my strong, Black warrior
inhaling the
> uncontrolled, unbridled
> unconditional
> noncorporate
> deprogrammed

passion cries...
of a man who feels temporary release
from *their* bondage.

CHARLES McGILL

On Leading a Cheer
for the Old Home Team

Keep on doin' it, brother!
Stand the ground of your belief.
Those who claim to own your land
    won't give you much relief.

Keep on doin' it brother!
Your whole culture's under fire.
They're taking gold and diamonds,
    leaving you the muck and mire.

Hang on in there brother!
There's a master plan at stake.
With many crucial deadlines that
    the world demands you make.

Raise your weapon, proudly;
Raise your head a little more.
Charge into the battle, be prepared
    for full-scale war.

Encouragement, dear brother
Is the best that we can give.
Fight hard for Mother Africa,
    so all of us can live.

Wake Up and Smile

Wake up, my friends, and smile a bit;
The truth is on its way.
Freedom rings from every tower;
It's a brand new day.

Hear me my friends, open your eyes;
Let's unify a while.
Gather round the poetry;
Listen—wake up—and smile.

Big Beautiful Black Girl Lips

Big beautiful black girl lips! Mmm...Yummy!
Big beautiful black girl lips!
In full bloom! In full effect! Fully erect lips!
Like plump little hearts—sweet tarts!—stretched wide across
The face. The most desirable lips in the human race!
No monkey or ape ever had lips like these...Mr. Darwin!
External lips, full-plump-purple-plum-like lips are a decidedly
Human trait! Made for love and affection, with affection and love
In mind! Two of a kind! Fine! Big! Beautiful! Black! Brown! Red!
Velvet! Sofa-like lips!
Love seats...that I would love my lips to be seated on!
To lie on! Fly on! And even die on!
Big beautiful black girl lips!
Your lips are still kissing me now! They never stop, somehow,
Leaving an impression on my soul!
Juicy fruit, never growing old, always fresh, wholesome lips!
Give me some lips that a man can sink his teeth into!
Lips that call from your attention without saying a word!
Big beautiful black girl lips!
A sign of the times, some say,
That could be spent with those other lips further south!
But, hey, let me shut my mouth and go find a pair of those
Big beautiful black girl lips...
To kiss.

Nubian Nightmare

he's a Mac Daddy running through the streets
spitting freestyle verse
he's a nickel plated smoker who has told death
"Get out of my face, I ain't scared of you"
he's a lawless, sassy ass that riddles his rhymes
for decoding by his homey
he's a mathematical genius
who adds his drug sales in his head
because he's been taught you'll get caught
if you leave a paper trail behind
he's a slung hip baggy pant wearer
who ain't thinking about capping his Willie
when he and his woman do the "Wild Thing"
he's a indigo tattoo stained artist
who can create a beautiful mural from memory
he's a blunt smoking adolescent
talking smack while grinding
his hips to some Reggae
he's a dehumanized victim
down on his knees at every corner
being questioned by the police
he's a flat bellied bulging firecracker
whose temper explodes when asked
"What are you doing down here strolling on Venice Beach?"
he's a Jetta, Cherokee Wagon, BMW, Lexus driver
who may not live long enough to pay a car note
he's the urban cowboy riding the range
from Florence and Normandie to Compton Boulevard
he's the new spoke and wheel disabled
rolling over anything that gets in his way
he's the non-planned parenthood participant
who loves his kids

he's the ready to work
unemployed minimum wage earner
he's the fast food "King of the Hill"
who rarely gets a physical
he's a political agitator
who won't let America forget
that without justice there can be no peace

Ambivalence

I felt your eyes, Dark Sister,
Boring through me
Now I see you,
Looking daggers my way
And willing my demise
(with my big Black self)
As I stroll
With this blond white girl,
With her big big baby blues
Looking up at me,
Looking up TO me;
Caressing the very soul
Of the Coloured boy inside
Her pale pink hand
Held firmly in my own.
Holding. Holding on.
To my forbidden fruit.

So pridefully
Did I strut
With this fi-i-i-i-ne
White girl
Until just this very moment
When I looked DEAD
Into your hard brown eyes
Eyes hard as stone
Yet misty, too,
And sad
And filled with RAGE! RAGE!
Today I feel your pain
Your RAGE! RAGE!
Damn!

I sense the welling up
Of hot, briny tears
Lurking just beyond the facade
Of the neck-rollin' finger-poppin'
Nay-sayin' StrongBlackSisterWoman
Thang!

Today I will not find
The words to name you:
JEALOUS BLACK GIRL!
As I did yesterday
And the day before
And the day before that...
Whenever our paths have crossed.

Hot shame, regret and sorrow
Sear my soul this day;
Wash over me, permeate my core,
My essence, and my being.
Now *my* hot, briny tears escape
And meander aimlessly
Down either side
Of my big Black nose.

Today; today I understand
Today she has to go
She has to go—
If I am to be there for you—
Damn!

Moody Woman Blues

I'm a moody woman, Lord, moody all the time
Yes, I'm a moody woman, so moody all the time
I tell it true when I say it
I need a strong man ta keep me in line
  I can wake up in the mornin'
  An' before I git out of bed
  Ma spirit's on its way down
  An' the devil's got ma head
Yes, I'm a moody woman
So moody all the time
I tell it true when I say it
I need a strong man ta keep me in line
  If we go out to a party
  An' ma man starts ta lookin' 'round alot
  I feel a mood comin' on me
  An' ma temper gittin' hot
Yeah, I'm a moody woman
I'm moody all the time
I ain't lyin' when I say that
I need a good man ta keep me in line
  I might be sittin' on ma doorstep
  An' the rain begins ta fall
  Don't say nothin' to me
  'Cause then I'm moodiest of all
Lord, I'm a moody woman
Moody all the time
I tell it true when I say it
I need a strong man ta keep me in line
  When I come home in the evenin'
  Ain't nothin' there but the four walls
  Ya know I'm restless as can be
  Until my Baby calls
Moody, moody, moody
So moody all the time
I'm still lookin' 'round ta find me
A soulful man ta keep me in li-i-ine...

The Lie in Dorcas Gin

For Zan and I to have met at any other time or in any other place except on that starlit, moonbright road in Dorcas Gin would not have seemed right. It was the best of times for me to see him again—and the worst of times for him. It took years of struggle to bring out the best in me: To define myself and release the real person. While I went through those changes, celibacy was highly desirable. But the loneliness of years of oneness was almost my undoing that night in Dorcas Gin. Being who I needed to be was my salvation.

Dorcas Gin. Home. It was a strangely peaceful place to work on my book. Houses that had throbbed with life were tumbling down in rebellion against their abandonment. Only a few old people were still there, cared for by relatives—young women who were too poorly educated to make it in the depression of the 1990s. The dreams of something better died in them as slowly as the old folks they fed the soft, bland foods and pills that kept them alive. There but for the Grace of God I might have been if my mother had not joined the exodus of the young who left Dorcas Gin during WWII. The girls went to the nearby town of Huaco, Texas in search of jobs, and mates with smooth, uncalloused hands. The boys went into the Army or the Navy.

Ready at last for a man enlightened enough to deal with this new person I had become, I came to a manless place. The only one there was pushing a walker in front of him to keep from falling down. Now the man I had always thought of as mine in my innermost secret self came striding toward me out of the night. Zan and I had lost each other thirty-two years before. Whatever went wrong between us was due to something missing in myself that left me as unfinished as a puzzle with some of the pieces gone. And the lie.

At first I wasn't sure it was he. The chance of meeting your first love on a deserted country road is as slim as you hope you'll be after three months of Chocolate, Strawberry and Vanilla Ultra-Slim. Our steps quickened toward each other. The light, lithe walk, the way he held his head cocked just slightly to the right, one shoulder a smidgin higher than the other couldn't belong to anyone except him. For forty-three years he had meant almost as much to me as I had to myself. I did not care that my belly poked out more than I wanted it to or that my eyes no longer shone with the clear, blueish white of unspoiled innocence. This man remembered the day I was born. He knew my name before I did.

We just looked at each other and shook our heads from side to side.

"I been thinking bout you. Now whut you doing down here on the day I moved back, Melissa?" he said, cocking his head sideways and smiling to let me know he was teasing, but wanting an answer that pleased him. I still knew that much about him.

So I took a step back, put both hands on my hips, leaned backward a little from the waist the way Black women do when they flirt, and said, "Lo-oo-oking for you."

He just grinned at me and held his arms open. I walked into them as naturally as I had that spring night when our love first began. We'd long gotten past the boy/girl phase of insulting each other. Our friendship kept growing when I came to Dorcas Gin every summer. One night outside the church I felt a slight chill and Zan unbuttoned his doubled-breasted suit jacket, opened it wide, pulled me to him, and wrapped me inside it with his arms. We knew then and there that we loved each other. Knew, and did not care about the obstacles we faced.

We tried so hard to keep our love secret. When the grown folks found out their hard, sharp disapproval could have driven a wedge between us. But we were too much in love to be wrong.

I guess Zan and me were meant to be two halves of a whole. We were both kind of outsiders in Dorcas Gin. His landless daddy owned the village juke-joint in the middle of cotton-country landowners. I lived in town and was considered unnaturally smart for a girl, which did not endear me to my country kin. We both had a place there, yet never quite belonged. It belonged to us though, in the way a place does where your afterbirth is buried. Nobody should have been surprised when we started loving each other. And we didn't care about age or objections.

It wasn't too long fore everybody in Dorcas Gin but my grandpa knew what was going on. If he'd known, he'd have half killed me. If my daddy had found out, he'd a bout killed the other half.

Zan's stepmama, my Aunt Rachel, came right out with it one Sunday after church. "The Elders," she told me, "decided to go ahead on and let yaw'll court. Ain't nobody going to tell your people bout you and Zan cause we can see ain't nothing nobody can do gonna stop yaw'll." Aunt Rachel wasn't none too happy bout the whole thing herself. "First thing," she said, "you ain't got no business courtin. You thirteen and Zan's a man of nineteen. Second thing, yaw'll too close to being cousins since I done raised him. I don't know what he want with no skinny behind girl black as you is no way." She shook her finger in my face. "Mind now, you keep your dress tail down and your drawers up, you hear?" Finger in my face, "I don't want to hear nothin bout you coming up in the family way and bout no shotgun wedding." She smiled proudly. "Zan goin be the first college graduate from Dorcas Gin."

I looked down at the ground like I was supposed to when an older person was talking to me. "Yes, Ma'am," I answered dutifully, and went on in the church to BYPU meeting.

We had three summers to fall deeper in love and the dark road was our private place. Every night I went out walking by myself and Zan met me. It was something I did all the time so my folks paid no attention to it. I was a child in love, doing things like running with a jar full of fireflies, pretending they were lanterns when we courted on that road. He'd laugh and chase me. Most times we'd just walk along holdin hands and talkin.

I had to go home when school started in the fall. It was much harder to find ways to be together in town. We found them though. Our favorite place was the picture show. We met there twice a week and on Saturday afternoons. Our first kiss was in the show.

Our third summer was almost over when my mother died. Some of my daddy's people was down there from California, visitin like they did every year. They wasn't going to hear nothin nobody had to say cept how much they could do for me, send me to college and all. I wanted to go. I didn't want to leave Zan, but I had to go. Had to leave a place where people called me crazy for saying things like there was television sets and you could watch shows in your own living room just like at the picture show. That's whut happened, they said, from keeping my head in a book all the time. As much as I hurt at the thought of leaving Zan, I wasn't missing a chance to go to California to live with relatives who had television and books in their house. Not with college dangling under my nose.

"Uh uhhh," Zan said when I told him I was leaving. "You ain't going when you got plenty of people to stay with right here."

"I want to go," was all I could say. I wasn't but fifteen years old. How could I know how to say that if I stayed there that something missing in me would never get found? Back then Negroes didn't go around talking about some pieces of themselves being missing. Folks would have thought I was crazy for real.

"I thought you loved me! You can't go off and leave me if you love me," he argued.

"I love you," I said, "but I have to get away from this place. I always wanted to get away from here."

"You ain't said nothin bout it before now." He had a puzzled look on his face. "Whut's wrong with it?" How could I answer a question like that? I did not possess the words that could make him see how stifling it was living in the buckle of the Baptist Bible Belt.

"How come you want to go off and leave me?" Zan asked.

"I don't want to leave you! I just want to go to California." I was crying. I wanted both. He gave a choking laugh, said, "I ain't never gonna forgive you if you leave," and walked away.

Two days later, my aunt and uncle took me to Los Angeles. I didn't see Zan for a long homesick year. Korea happened and he went into the army. We lived on letters.

The next summer he was there on furlough when we went to visit. I went back to L.A. no longer a virgin. But neither of us promised to be faithful. He wasn't. My cousins wrote that he was seeing another girl everytime he went home on furloughs. I started going with a boy I met in college. I got pregnant. We married. Then Zan married, got out of the army and moved to Detroit.

I still loved him.

It was six years before I saw him again. And still full of the training I hadn't been in California long enough to lose. I was visiting folks in Dorcas Gin who'd missed church that Sunday. No one told me he was there visiting too. My three-month-old baby was cuddled in my arms. My two-year-old and four-year-old were sitting there as politely as they'd been taught to do in company. His folks were busy congratulating me on my fine family and my youthful appearance after three children in five years. I was supposed to look worn out, have lost three teeth, gained twenty pounds and look like I was expecting gray hair any day.

Zan stomped in. He didn't speak to nobody. He just looked at me, then at my three children like they should have been his and asked one urgent question. "You still with your husband?"

Tradition tied my tongue. Women in Dorcas Gin didn't leave their husbands. I could not, after his folks had just said how well I looked like I was doing, admit that I had left mine. Folks in California were supposed to be rich, but my daddy had to send me a round-trip ticket I was so broke. I lied.

"Yes," I said, and wondered for twenty-four years why I did.

He turned such a look of rage on me before he walked out that I felt like somebody threw scalding hot water in my face. I wanted to get up out of that chair, run out of that house, grab him and say, "I'm not with my husband anymore, come back to California with me!" Southern Negro convention cemented me to that chair. A woman did not run after a man. Or, was it those unfound missing pieces making me feel like a partial person that forced out that "yes?"

After my children grew older I finished college. Black Studies classes led me on the search for my cultural identity. I finally found those "missing" pieces through learning our history and growing to become the person I had a right to be. It was so good for me and so good to me that I felt most men would complicate it and make me miserable because I couldn't be what they wanted. Becoming a whole, complete person meant a lot, but it didn't give me anybody warm to snuggle up to every night.

So when I met Zan on the road, hope rose up as though I could grasp it along with a handful of stars from the night sky. Here was somebody that a part of me had never stopped loving, standing in the middle of the road, holding me in the old familiar way.

I broke away and looked up into his barely-brown, freckled face. "Come on," I said. "I fixed up grandpa's house and I'm staying there. You want to go on up there and have a cold beer?"

"Sure," he said. We walked up the road holding hands like we used to do. After he was settled on the sofa with his beer, he asked, "So whut you doing down here? Don't tell me the California girl came home?"

"No, I'm down here for a few months to work on a book." But that twenty-four year old lie was determined to get up off my conscience. I blurted out, "I got to ask you something."

"Whut," Zan said, grinning in anticipation.

For the first time that night I felt shy. "The last time I saw you," I began stammering, "that time at your daddy's house when you asked me if I was still with my husband. What would you have done if I'd said no?"

He looked surprised. "What made you ask me that?"

"Because I lied. I was getting a divorce. I always wondered what would have happened if I'd told you the truth."

He actually squirmed. "I don't know. I felt like grabbing you and your kids and getting out of there. But, I would have remembered my wife and kids pretty damn quick." He sighed. "I guess you heard she died last year. You did right to lie about it. It wouldn't have done anybody any good if you hadn't."

"What a relief! It's been on my mind all of these years."

"Well, now you can stop worryin bout it. So, you're writin a book. I heard you got educated. Whut kind of book you writin?"

"It's really about Dorcas Gin, about what happened here."

"Did somethin happen here?" he asked, surprised.

"Everyday. You remember the 'Gin' was founded by my great-great-grandmother, Dorcas? Do you have any idea what it took to keep the whites from getting this land all those years? People died for it, killed to keep it, almost killed themselves working to hang onto it. The book is really a tribute to all of the people in little communities all over the South who did the same thing. I'm talking to the old folks about it before they die off and all of that history gets lost forever."

"How come you want to write a book bout all that old stuff?"

"Cause, it's part of us. It's our heritage from them."

"Uh-huh," he took a swallow of beer. I could see he wasn't getting it. "Come on over here and sit by me so I can tell you how pretty you still are. You find the fountain of youth or what?"

"Naw, I just live right," I laughed.

He put his arm around me. My head fell into its natural place. "You know I never stopped lovin you, don't you?" he whispered in my ear. "I done waited long enough for you."

I knew what he wanted to hear. I was supposed to say I still loved him, but the words wouldn't leave my mouth.

"Look," I had to keep trying to make him understand. If he could relate to my work, my Afrocentricity, maybe we could have a chance. "My great-great grandmama Dorcas was African. She and one son worked, saved and bought this land. Others whose names are lost did as well or better. They were strong people because the people that were taken from Africa as slaves were the young and strong; the smartest, the best. They passed those genes down through the generations to us. We have to teach our young..."

"Woman, will you shut up so I can kiss you? I don't want to hear nothin bout no Africa." He pulled me closer, saying, "I was a manager at the plant when I retired, get a good check every month. The house was paid for, made a ni...ice piece of change when I sold it. We can buy a new car every year and build us a fine new house. That'll keep you too busy to think bout all this nonsense you talkin bout."

"You've done well, Zan. New car every year, huh? Sounds like the good life."

"Yeah, I did right well in Detroit," he said proudly.

I let it drop. His mind was still enslaved by our brainwashed past of negroness that was instilled in most Southern children.

He kissed the tip of my nose. Those years of celibacy were a passion-rising clash with my hard won beliefs. He kissed me and I was putting everything I had into kissing him back. I never wanted our lips to part.

"No," I panted and moved away. "I can't live down here! And you know, don't you, that you want your woman in that nice new kitchen rattling those pots and pans? Now you know I never been the domestic type," I tried to make a joke of it.

"Please please please don't do this to me again!" he cried.

"I'm not doing it to you, I'm doing it for me!"

He didn't know what I was talking about. He'd never understand my connection with our African ancestors, our African American fore-parents. My strength came from the recognition and appreciation of them, of what they had endured in order to survive so we could thrive. I couldn't waste all of that to become an unhappy homemaker. I had books to write.

I thought of the years it took for me to cleanse from my mind the shame of being Black, the low self-esteem that the Southocracy so competently instilled in us as children, to understand how colorism and classism had been used to create a chasm between some of us, how self-hatred and materialistic values instead of self-love led our drugged youth to participate in their own genocide.

"Zan," I said softly, trying to reach through his pain, "I worked hard for years to raise my children. At jobs just for the paycheck." I poked a finger into my chest. "Now I'm doing what I want to do. I can't give that up to worry about your meals and if you have clean underwear in your drawer. That's not...me, it never was. Can't you understand that?"

A light dawned in his eyes. "So it wasn't me all those years ago when you left. You don't want any man, do you? Damn! You'd have saved me a lot of heartache if you'd told me that back then." He stood up to leave.

"Yes, Zan, I want a man, and you I wanted always." I closed my eyes on his pain. "Always. But I want one who knows who he is. That I can share everything with—love, mind, body, soul, work—one to grow with." I turned away. "I can't be what you need."

"I don't even know what you talkin bout. You read too much," he said, standing in the door looking at the shelves filled with books. "I guess it drove you crazy like everybody said it would." I said goodbye to the man who as a child looked into my newborn face and said, "She's a pretty baby to be so dark." He slammed the door and took away with him the years of pain from my heart.

I bet he didn't even know how to find Africa on a globe.

On the Shoulders of Time

Standing on the shoulders of my ancestors
I gaze upon the horizon
at the world
my oyster

an oyster whose pearl was glazed
with the blood of my people
many years ago—
who
torn from the Motherland
toiled in hot sun and inclement weather
from morning till night
under conditions so harsh
it hurts to remember
but who
through all the adversity
never gave up
the dream of freedom

On the shoulders of my ancestors
I gaze into the past
to become better acquainted
with the future assured me
by
those whose tears fell like
raindrops upon barren land
as loved ones
were sold like cattle
the multitude who felt
the sharp sting of the whip
with each breath taken
and
those who sacrificed with their lives
so that generations coming after
would not know the same injustices

I see—
chains of slavery
binding the body
but not the mind—
a determination
to survive despite
all attempts to break the spirit—
the desire to overcome greater
than day-to-day sufferings
and
the realization that a rightful existence
must be forged in a land
that prospered on the broken backs
of many.

The shoulders on which I stand
are very strong
from
many nights huddled around candlelight
learning how to read
countless days grasping each skill learned
a relentless dedication to
underground railroads
run at the risk of death
and
seeds lovingly planted in the midst of despair
that brought forth
educators, politicians, writers, and inventors
with a strong sense of purpose

Perseverance and determination
best describes the shoulders
on which I proudly stand
while listening to
the whispers of long ago about
hardships conquered
suffering endured
obstacles surmounted
and faith held strong

I will forever hear—
the songs of my ancestors whose very existence
set in motion
a chain of events that forever
changed the course of history
and laid the groundwork
for all to follow and strive
toward their rightful place in the sun.

Man of Tomorrow...

The man of tomorrow will need

a luggage rack for his attaché.

He'll need metal lined pockets

to carry his pocket phone.

He'll need a carrying case for his organizer.

And be in shape to carry it all.

Red's Rhythm

Boy, what you know about dancing? Just 'cause you got a little college beyond your belt don't mean you the best stepper on the floor. Why, if she were still livin', your grandma could have told you about me—but I don't know if she would have.

In my time, they called me Red. I was mercurial...hot as blue fire. I could reel on swamp mud at two hundred miles an hour and stop straight up on a Canadian dime. I used to spin my body so fast that I would'a drilled a hole clean through that floor you're high-steppin' on, and the sparks flyin' from my taps would'a scared all the critters away from under the house.

You don't believe me, do you? Well listen up!

Back in New Orleans, in-folk supped jazz music for lunch and imbibed it for dinner to wash down gumbo so spicy hot it would make you sweat. So usually when the last set ended at the High Seven Club, the hip cats—after gumbo, jazz, and wine—strutted through the door mopping their faces with oversized handkerchiefs. The ladies of course had powdered up and cooled off long before the music stopped.

One Saturday night, me and Raynell "Dizzy" Williams, exited the High Seven and made our way toward an after-hours jam I had been invited to by a sweet cube of sugar named Sarah G. who, earlier in the evening, had tried her best to keep up with me on the dance floor. We finally made it to the joint—a ritzy multistory tenement that looked like a private museum. As soon as I knocked on the door, the brass peephole squeaked open. I felt eyes and air poring through on me.

"Red here. Sarah G. plugged me."

The door opened and big Charlie Downs, dock worker by day and bouncer by night, towered over me with a grin.

"My man, Red, the jazzy high-stepper."

"The one and only." I removed my cocked Panama from my slicked-down hair. "And this here is my running ace, Dizzy."

"Y'all come on through."

"Solid."

I flipped Charlie two bits, and me and Dizzy eased down the hallway toward the sound of the groove. Before we could figure which way to go, a smiling petite waitress wearing a tight skirt above her knees had come up and handed me a glass of watered-down whisky on the rocks.

"Hi, mister high-stepper."

"Hi to you, doll. Red's my name."

"Everybody knows that."

Dizzy lifted a drink for himself from the tray and replaced it with a coin.

"And you can call me Dizzy."

The waitress thanked Dizzy for the tip and kept making her rounds.

I looked around at the hip people in the room we had landed in, gestured a toast, downed my shot of whiskey in a single swallow, then looked over at the waitress for a refill.

Only the squares didn't get juiced. Red was no square, so I got down, real down—high as Benjamin Franklin's kite. A few more shots of whiskey layered on early evening wine had me feelin' good as a pig in slop. There I was tripping off the funny lights in a large multidimensional room peppered with in-folk. The players huddled in corners floating in their baggy pleated pants and flashing their gold watch chains. A few cats leaned so far forward that if their ladies didn't prop 'em up, they'd fall flat on their mugs.

Dizzy got caught up in a lively corner discussion with a few musician acquaintances who couldn't resist trying to unravel Charlie Parker's solos. So I got my swollen, woozy head out of that scene and hitched a ride here and there on some of those ad hoc confab cliques continually forming and dismantling in other corners, in other rooms, on upper floors, and on the roof.

A cool breeze swirled around on the roof. But hot music and jammed-tight congestion warmed all bodies—big bodies, little bodies, wide and short bodies, tall bodies, curvaceous bodies, blob bodies, liquid and some dry bodies, lean and foaming bodies, scented bodies, working bodies, somebodies, and nobodies. I bet you didn't know there was that many different kind of bodies. They had more than that congregating on the roof that summer morning, but I just can't remember them right off.

Then there was one lovely body I'll never forget. I can see her this very moment the way I saw her that night way back yonder ... stuffed like Louisiana hot sausage, seasoned with sage and other mouth-watering spices. I can see her just as clearly as I can see you slip and slide and jerk across them varnished wooden slats on your mama's living room floor. Early that Sunday morning, the lady circled deliciously about a barrel of fire center roof to the beat of a seductive number blaring out of the arch-headed jukebox. Hundreds of skinny braids flung about her aerodynamic noggin like an iridescent tether ball seen through hallucinating eyes. Liquid magic flew from each twirling braid.

The crowd barked with pleasure, clapped and egged her on.

I said to myself, what is this wholesome, beautiful goddess doing shaking her lithe physique that way? I couldn't believe such a tall, wide, curvaceous body could be so foaming, working, and liquid. She had to be into yoga, aerobics, voodoo, or something. This thing she was working on churned my machismo. What she was doing was Red's kind of thing. Congo Square ain't gone nowhere.

Gingerly I pranced out to center roof and emphatically introduced myself.

"Red here, baby! What you say?"

She looked me straight in the eye and smiled. "You is red, ain't you, but are you hot?"

What was she looking at? A sunburned grape? She could not have been looking at me. I am not red; this shirt is red.

I peeled off my suede jacket, draped it across my shoulder, and primed up for the lady's sultry challenge.

"Didn't I say my name was Red?"

"Yeah. But are you red-dy?"

"Anytime. Any way. I was born steppin', and ain't nothing slowed me down yet."

I slung my jacket across the room, undid the top buttons on my red silk shirt, and bared my heaving chest. Then I snapped my fingers in beat with the polyrhythmic sounds that lit up the roof and the blackened sky.

She faced my way and snapped her fingers, too.

"Well, honey, get down and hit it. 'Cause if you can't hit it, you can't get it."

I wanted to ask "Get what?" It would have been a natural question, but square as a checkerboard. Red was too cool for that. Snapped my fingers to the beat and dipped my knees. That's what I did.

Suddenly I whirled my body around slowly. I had one hand all the way down fingers snapping, and I had the other hand all the way up fingers snapping. I moved about her smoldering, gyrating mass to map out the territory, all the while smiling and peering into her large, airy dark eyes, mindful that the popping crowd was gearing up for show time. Those who knew my reputation chanted my name. "Red," they said. But to my surprise, some high cascading voices in the crowd echoed brick house's name cacophonously.

"Ruby, Ruby."

"Ru-bay, honey get down."

Then I heard Sarah G.'s voice.

"Ruby, show that stud a thing or two, but not too much, 'cause he learns real fast."

Ruby! The name caught my ear. They say she had been all over twisting that wonderfully supple body. In Harlem at the Savoy. In Los Angeles at Club Alabam. Now I was looking at her with my very own eyes. Uptown and down. Live and in person. Done tasted the salt of the Atlantic and the Pacific. Ruby. Come to conquer Orleans.

But Orleans was my town! Me, Red, who hung out with the high-steppin' Copas and blew all the young girls' minds with my flying feet and mercurial hips.

So I told her again, "Red's my name, baby. Yeah. From coast to coast. Every day." All the while, I still snapped my fingers low and high while circling my prey.

She moved toward me as if she were gliding through air. Then she caught me off guard with her magical smile, banged my poor little mesmerized body hard with her thick hips, and whispered within a hot breath of my lips.

"Olé."

Just look at your grandpa. Don't look like it, but I used to be the baddest ace of spades ever 'lit on that Creole plantation. Me, Red. Could spin so fast on my tips that if I didn't stop, next thing you'd hear a siren come to put out the fire. I was good. When I got good and hot, they called me Red. At my peak, I scorched...turned ice blue. Then they called me Cool Red. And God gave Noah the rainbow sign, no more water, Red next time.

You don't believe me, do you?

Well anyway, son, the truth is that dancing and rhythm are glued together with life...like red beans and rice. And during the hardest of times—which I've had my share of in this life of mine—rhythm can dress up the worst kind of noise.

Long before you ever think about getting as old as me, you're going to find out that you can no longer hang your cool on the golden hanger. That's when you'll move over to silver or copper. You may even lose a step or two. Take the day your mother came into this world. I can see her now...her soft little body curled up in your grandma's arms. That was the day I gave up trippin' and juicin' altogether and settled down like regular folks.

But the rhythm that started in me is still in me. It's all up in my head and ain't go'n never go away. It defines and creates the harmony in my soul. It's a gift, an inheritance that moves along from generation to generation. I can hear it in your music and see it in your dance. And no matter how many college degrees you end up getting, that rhythm will always be with you.

Just to think, it all started in the wee hours of a warm Sunday morning when a pretty lump of sugar banged my hips and had me stumbling around a barrel of fire. I'll tell you the truth. Your grandma Ruby wore me out on that roof. But she fixed my soul for keeps. Sweetness, goodness, may she forever rest in peace.

Going Greyhound

As I sat looking out of the window
while riding from New Orleans
through Mobile
Birmingham
Montgomery
Atlanta
I thought of the places
where my people toiled
were lashed
beaten and killed
where sit-ins
marches and protests
were staged
where Black folks still linger
in poverty

And I said to myself
oh
what beautiful country
With such a brutal past

Fannie Lou Hamer:
A Rock in a Weary Land

Fannie Lou, at the age of six,
began her life in Rule
Picking cotton in this Delta town:
It was her learning school.
She sharecropped and she kept the time
eighteen long, hard years,
Her path was strewn with barriers-
And often bitter tears.
Yet, she was a rock in a weary land,
and early on, we note
They fired her from the old plantation
for trying to cast a vote.

A fearful life she had to live,
And threatened time again;
Sixteen bullets riddled the house
where she hid with a kindly friend.
Ms. Hamer was often brutalized
by the minions of segregation,
She tried to use the restroom
at the old Trailway bus station,
For this she was brutally beaten
and forcibly dragged away
To the jailhouse in Winona,
She was crippled to her dying day.

She led a delegation
to challenge the lily-white seat
At the demo convention in Jersey-
she refused to accept defeat;
She won a pledge from the party
that in nineteen sixty-eight
No blacks would be excluded
from the ballot in her state.
She even ran for Congress,
but 'ol Miss' held her back,
Then she authored the "Freedom Ballot"
to serve both white and black.

She lost her fight for Congress,
yet was first to sit on the floor
Of the house with two other women,
Their courage broke open the door.
A fighter and a dynamo
in the field of civil rights,
Not only Mississippi, but
the nation acclaims her fights.
She was indeed a hammer,
though bloody, she made her stand
For freedom, conscience and justice:
A rock in a weary land.

An Ole Cypress Song

Quiet as it's kept, there's a tale told more often than not on a cold clear winter's night in some old griot's den. An old cajun mother's Christmas fable told in whispers and dialect to her children's children as they cluster about a fire, huddled in blankets and holding candles as protection against the dark. The light of the candles flicker and fade as the storyteller is coaxed by a child whose eyes are filled with dreams of magic and love.

"What kind of story you want to hear?" the teller asks.

"Love!"

"Hoodoo!"

"Adventure!"

The requests are called out eagerly, but it is the first request that makes the teller pause and tilt her head thoughtfully "Love?"

"Yes love," a young girl on the brink of womanhood insists.

The young men in the room grumble and protest, but are hushed by the griot.

"I'll tell you a winter's tale of love. But it's not the kind of love your parents read you out of fairy tales, nor the kind of young spring infatuation quickly come and gone. It's a courageous, tragic love. So begins this tale..."

In church every Sunday, children and adults are instructed about the power of prayer. The act of humbly entreating your God to grant your deepest wishes and inner desires. This story is a warning and a testimony to the power of prayer. When kneeling down on your knees at night remember these words and take care what you pray for you might get it.

Now it's always been supposed that salt-water fish don't take to the bayou waters. The vegetation and undergrowth just aren't conducive to them. But it's also known that you can find all manner of creatures in the bayou. Two-headed toads and three-legged gators don't surprise swamp Cajuns, but there are some creatures that turn even the most experienced conjure man's head.

Never on a night like this, but sometimes on a fog-drenched late summer's eve a soft singing can be heard floating up from the bayou. Those that don't know imagine it's a lost songbird. But anyone who stops to listen knows better. Sometimes the singer will let a child or a young man catch a glimpse of her person. Always the viewer is startled to see what looks like a mulatto woman of about eighteen or nineteen immersed in the water. Only her silky dark hair, luminous eyes and graceful arms can be clearly seen. Should the viewer come too close, the woman vanishes and her song is silence. Any calls to wait or offers of help are ignored and the viewer doubts his or her sanity. It's said she was a runaway slave girl who begged the ancient gods to hide her from her hunters in the swamp. She never found her way out again. Once, however, the lady listened and remembers being enchanted by a jazz man's song.

This jazz man played the saxophone and was widely known in every club and juke joint from New Orleans to New York. In his music was the blood of the South. His playing evoked memories of an outdoor summer dance on a hot, starlit night, the flavor and frolic of a first Mardi Gras or the wonder of love on the bayou. His name's well known in the small parish where he was born, and there's a memorial to him in Lafayette Cemetery. Whether he truly rests in peace is a mystery.

One night he happened to hear the swamp girl's song. Enchanted, he joined her by imitating her notes with his saxophone. She listened, and then began to sing along with him for a while until she stopped abruptly. All he heard was a splash of water and she was gone.

There was no help for it, she was gone. The jazz man couldn't find her that night or the next. But her music stayed with him and when he played it in the clubs the listeners were moved to tears.

The second time he heard her music, he only played a few notes before she joined in. Her soft voice picked up the melody and even added new variations to it. He was so enthralled by her singing that he stopped playing. As soon as the music stopped, she halted her song and waited for him to continue.

"Come out, and I'll play as long as you like!"

There were ripples across the water and slowly he saw the shadows part to make way for a lovely young woman. She was soaked in swamp water from head to toe and moss clung to the thin green cotton of her dress. Her long black hair curled and clung to her shoulders. The jazz man had sat down and was leaning against a tree whose roots stretched out to the river. She dropped softly beside him and reached out to touch the smooth brass of his saxophone. He sat motionlessly, transfixed and unable to talk while she examined his instrument. After what seemed an eternity she spoke softly in the lilting accent of the Cajuns, "Play again, please."

He could only do as she asked. He played till his throat grew dry and the sun began to rise over the river. As the first ray of sunlight grazed her, the woman, who had said nothing else, fled back into the river before he could stop her.

The jazz man carried news of the woman throughout the parish and into the town to anyone who would listen. When he had first heard her song, he imagined it was some strange bird's bizarre ballad. When he sought to share the truth of the swamp singer, he was met with coldness and impassivity.

To his dismay he could not find her again. He slowly drifted into a world of solitude constantly haunted by her voice and beauty. His music lacked the luster and spirit it once had. No more did it inspire lovers to kiss in the audience or women to pull their men from their chairs to dance. Instead, tears and silent weeping were the applause he received.

His existence wasn't the only life troubled. The swamp girl was as enchanted as the musician. Her dreams were haunted by a music with skin the color of moist earth and magical golden instrument. Seeking freedom from her watery prison, she sought the counsel of a local priestess of Voudun.

The priestess was an ancient woman, so old it was thought she'd once been a slave. She had a habit of gathering herbs for her charms and medicine in the bayou where the swamp girl stayed. One afternoon, as she made her weekly rounds, a voice bid her take heed.

"Old mother, I crave freedom."

The priestess looked up suspiciously from her gathering, "What's that?"

"Old mother, I seek help."

Muttering to herself the priestess replied, "What you seek shall be yours. Is this music boy you love worth the roux in his gumbo?"

"Old mother, he is. Name your price."

Smiling the priestess said, "I can help you. And there's no price fo' this sort of work for me. The payment's in the charm. Catch!"

The old woman flung a small pouch out towards the swamp. There was a splash of water and a rustle among the reeds as the swamp girl dove for the pouch. Beneath the water she grasped the pouch between her hands and looped the leather string over her head. Shaking the moss from her hair the girl climbed up from the swamp to the dry ground where the priestess stood. She knelt and kissed the woman's hands.

"Thank you, I can't say how..."

"Hush chile, like I said. The payment's in the charm. You can come with me tomorrow to the market and sell crawfish. I tell him you my sister's daughter come from the islands. You'll get your man chile, but should he stray from your bed, or take you far from the swamp, you be returning to where you came from. Only you be less than a swamp rat and no more alive than the silt in the Mississippi."

"I'm willin' to risk that for him."

The swamp girl followed the priestess to her cabin by the river. There the woman gave her clothing and food. She slept for once beneath a roof of wood and not of stars, beside a fire and not within a watery blanket.

For the next several weeks the swamp girl sold crawfish in the market with the priestess. Her sweet voice often brought in more than the usual money and her beauty made gentlemen and tramps whether black, white, Creole, Cajun pause to admire and even presume to request her favors. The priestess smiled, shook her head and shattered their hopes stating, "She is not for you."

One later afternoon, the sensual melody of the saxophone came drifting through the streets of the market, accompanied by shouts and running feet. The jazz man had returned to New Orleans was the shout on the street. The people of the Vieux Carre had followed him down Conti Street and the river's edge where the market teemed with life and movement.

Amidst the voices of joy, the musician heard a soft voice sustain above the noise of the streets. Nearby, a hauntingly beautiful woman held a basket of crawfish in her arms which she graciously displayed to all who passed by. Entranced, the jazz man stopped beside her, kneeled down and began to play. Caught by memory, she began to sing and the jazz man was so overcome he could not play.

"Lady, I reckon' I've seen you before."

Before she could answer the priestess said, "Her name be Evangeline."

"Evangeline," he whispered softly and reached to take her hand.

The newly christened Evangeline placed her hand in his and sealed a promise. The priestess gave her a sprig of rosemary and kissed her cheek whispering, "Remember."

Evangeline smiled, bid her benefactress farewell and went with the jazz man. Needless to say, he married her. The joy came back into his song; the sadness and longing were gone and replaced with the security of love. It seems folks prefer listening to music that makes them fall in love over music that brings them to the edge of death. As a result, the jazz man became even more popular, famous and rich off his music. The folk loved his music, and they adored his gracious, obviously well-born wife, who was always at his side often singing with him at the clubs.

Yet always greed conspires against those so blessed to find both love and fortune. The jazz man did not continue to cherish his wife. As she had a fear of leaving Louisiana, and could not be moved to travel, the jazz man often went on tour without her. While he became richer and more well known in Harlem, Chicago and St. Louis, she remained in New Orleans often taking long walks along the bayou.

Her neighbors and the cityfolk thought her peculiar. "Did ya see her talkin' to the gators like them was her chillun'?" or "She ain't nothin' but mulatto trash anyhow." Since she never spoke of her past, the neighbors assumed the worst. They fancied she was the bastard daughter of a rich, white planter, married off and settled quietly. Or she was a voodoo queen stealthily practicing her arts unbeknownst to her husband. Whatever gossip, or rumor, they were not flattering.

In spite of their harsh words, the folk were always enchanted by her lonely singing, and many men made offers to her, often forceful. She steadfastly refused their advances always faithful to her husband.

Like most men, without his woman, the jazz man settled for substitutes. Silken women in cheap hotels, and high class whores in fancy suites, all replaced his Evangeline. When he returned from a particularly long trip, he found her sick in bed. Kneeling beside her he kissed her hand, "I'm back baby. Back for good this time."

Evangeline smiled weakly and gestured to the gold locket around her neck which contained the small pouch given to her so long ago. The gold was faded and tarnished.

Puzzled the jazz man asked, "What happened?"

"You been gone," she whispered and opened the locket.

It was empty.

"I'll make you get better. I'll never leave again, I promise..."

Evangeline did get better, but like so many promises her husband's was not kept. He soon left her again. This time when he left, Evangeline came with him. He stayed faithful with his wife beside him, but the city air seemed to draw the strength from Evangeline. Ultimately, she had to return. She left unwillingly, and after the jazz man swore to come home within a week. Once she returned home, Evangeline fell ill again.

Those rich white gentleman in the city, who had always desired her, made they way up to the house one night. They'd been drinking in the clubs and one fate-blind reckless waged a ridiculous sum of money to the man who could get her first. They broke into her home and forced her out into the swamp. Chasing her with dogs, and laughing they pursued her into the swamp. However, she ran so far and fast they finally gave up. But Evangeline did not stop, spurred on by memories of another life when she once before ran from hunters and deranged by her illness and solitude.

The torch light caressed her face, creating orange and black streaks across her cheeks and the bridge of her nose. The bronze flickering was the only light in the dim wetness of the cypress swamp. The fear that the light that guided her way might also reveal her concealment to the hunters was outweighed by the danger of tumbling into a marsh. She had no desire to be the next meal of a cluster of nutria rats or swamp gators.

As she climbed and half stumbled among the roots of the cypresses and wild undergrowth, her ears were perpetually cocked and alert. She imagined the barking of dogs and the clattering of hooves close behind her even though there'd been nothing but the chattering of birds and croaking of frogs.

The first rays of morning could be seen creeping up from the west and between the high canopy of leaves. Fear of discovery propelled her deeper into the swamp. She waded into the water and shaking, she pulled the now blackened locket from her neck and flung it behind her. Closing her eyes, she allowed the swamp to once again engulf her. This time she would not be reborn.

They never found her body. When the jazz man returned home, full of greetings and presents he found only a empty, demolished house and the priestess sadly shaking her head.

"Evangeline! Honey, I'm back! Where are you?"

"She's gone, man. Back to where she come from" the priestess held out her hand to him and inside was the blackened locket. The jazz man took the locket and tried rubbing it clean, but the blackness only spread till not a glimmer of the gold could be discerned.

Pushing aside the priestess, he took his saxophone and ran to the swamp. He fell on his knees beside the place where he first heard her song and began playing. He played throughout the day and into the night. The town folks murmured apologies to a man who had become a statue, frozen in his playing and obsessively listening for his song to be returned. It is not known whether or not he ever heard Evangeline's singing, but it was the priestess who came later to bury his body in Lafayette and to this day the tomb with its carving of rosemary and a gold locket is a reminder of a woman who risked her life for love and a man who was truer to his song than to himself.

"Some say you can still hear her song in the bayous, if you walk along the Mississippi late at night."

After a time, one listener, the same young woman who requested a tale of love remarked, "I wouldn't want to hear a song like that."

The teller smiled. "These tales are a guide to humankind, about people more courageous, loving and reckless than humans generally are, yet can always be. The songs are always there, but it takes a brave man to listen and return its melody."

Driving 27

Even though I couldn't see well at night, I caught the keys. Holding them in my hand, I felt something shift between Elliott and myself. I didn't expect Elliott to respond this way. I had given off too many signs. My moods. Depression. When he would ask, "You okay?", his eyes a bit wide, softly intense, I'd answer and say I was alright. Intense is how I would describe our relationship. Until I met Peter, I never knew how much this intensity had threatened to suffocate me. I love Elliott. But, I'm not in love with him. At this moment I'm in love with how he is reacting. He is actually angry. Passionate. Alive. Most of the time, and he even admitted it, he held his feelings in check, not because he didn't feel them but because he was always sensitive to what effect his feelings, once verbalized, had on the person, myself included. He told me that after six months of living together. I felt he had peeled away another layer of himself, exposing it for my view only. I loved that quality about Elliott. He had this wonderful way of making you feel that you were at the center of the universe when his spoken words traveled to your ears in whispers that rustled like the leaves on sleepy silver maples, each word floating over sparkles the sun held and then released. It's ironic, I'm thinking as I note to myself, that sometimes the biggest frustration of our relationship is communication.

I watch him standing there, his shoes sunk in the sand, the teasing waves a bit farther from him now that he moved a few seconds ago. Facing me, his clothes flap around him like sails wrapped around ships masts, the wind making his dreadlocks bob up and down sporadically with each gust. I was both angry and confused. I hadn't expected Elliott to react this way. We had been discussing the prospect of sleeping with other people for at least a couple of months. No more than a day or so after I met Peter. With Peter I thought it would be easier to say let's part. It was even Elliott who had brought it up. He'd flown to New York last month to meet with one of his clients and had ended up going to a bar after one of their midnight meetings. At one point, he told me later, his leg thrown over mine, lying in our bed that faced the darkened hilltop above Silver Lake, that he had gone so far as to walk the guy home, thinking to himself that he would sleep with him. He didn't. I hadn't really believed him then. I did now. Listening to the gurgly lull of the tide, I wanted, at this point, to be in his head, where I would open doors and drawers of his thoughts that I never would hear, my eyes afloat in hopes of getting to know him still. But I couldn't. I had maxed out my card. That made me angry. Just when I thought I was getting to know him, a movement or glance so familiar to him, alien in my eyes, would dart out, throwing off my balance as I wrestled with what comment had caused that angry reaction. I turned away as I felt the heat of Elliott's eyes cool toward me. He was hurting.

I felt the same way that Elliott did about water. Yet his view was so rich and primitive. Water's place in the South, he said to me, his light Southern accent making his words curl in spoken humidity, is one of cleansing and purification, most often used in religion. I remember that day. It was one of those rare Saturdays where we both had woken up with nothing planned. We hadn't talked too much throughout the day, just muttering sentences that trailed to nowhere, the kind that couples clothed themselves in. That afternoon, Elliott produced a six-pack of Budweiser and said that we were going to get drunk. Neither of us drank too often and two or three would help knock us out. Sitting outside under the shade, the typical cloudless Los Angeles day illuminating the white deck to a fluorescence, I had never felt so far away from the cars, smog and graffiti-covered walls, as I was when we traveled south and I became the sidewalk shadow in Elliott's childhood. I walked along the gravel roads, my feet crunching the dead leaves laid out as gifts, the towering magnolias scattered over them like brittle petals. Our breaths captured the frost in the air where words wisped into the bright fall morning, hovering, mist-like, over a frozen pond, its grass immobile, patiently waiting until spring wakened from slumber.

I took a deep breath and sighed, my hands shoved in my jeans, rubbing against the lean muscles of my legs. Swimmer's legs, I thought. I had been a swimmer since I was twelve. By no means was I a terrific swimmer, yet the years of practice made me pretty good. For me water was a dare to defeat. Potentially dangerous and fatal, I reveled in the soft pressure it wrapped me in, encapsulating my body into the light blue void. I really loved my time in the water. I always thought of falling in love with Elliott when my laps ran into infinity. I closed my eyes and felt my hair drape around my face as I realized I wasn't in love with him now. Shuddering, I turned toward Elliott and wished he would say we could go. I hated being cold.

"This is so bitchin, dude," I said, breaking the silence that had shrouded us heavier than the darkness. I said generic things when I didn't know what to say. Even as a child, I chose that route and I still do it now. I learned that it's usually easier to survive by not saying much. Experience in being shuffled from home to home, praying that someone would adopt you, teaches you that. Until my brother and I were adopted, I never said what I meant because I was always so afraid of being sent back to the orphanage. Spontaneous abandonment. That's the only emotion I felt through my childhood. I blinked my eyes, realizing I initiated the same action with Elliott. I waited for him to answer as the silence prodded unwanted memories. Elliott said nothing. His hand dove into his pocket and I knew that we would leave soon. He tossed his car keys to me.

"What's this?" I said, catching them. I didn't really want to drive. My eyes always dried out after I drove Elliott's car. Maybe he had forgotten.

"It's your turn to drive," he said, walking back to the car. I wanted to talk to him but I knew that he wasn't in a mood to talk. He stood by the passenger side and I walked up.

"I don't feel like driving," he said and climbed into the passenger seat, tossing his head before putting on his seatbelt.

With that motion, I knew that we wouldn't talk much during the ride. That was a sign he was fuming. I pushed back the seat and stretched my legs forward into the car. Elliott's steering wheel was one-third smaller than the regular one in most convertible Bugs. When I first drove his car, I always felt like I was turning too fast, until I realized that I had to turn twice as much. I backed up out the parking lot and headed for Pacific Coast Highway. Elliott was bent over his seat, fumbling for tapes in his glove compartment.

"Which one are you looking for?" I said, my eyes glued to my rearview mirror while I merged into traffic.

"Just a tape," Elliott said. He picked one up and held it up as we passed underneath a street light.

I heard him taking out the earlier cassette and pushing in the one he had chosen. Another "Everything But The Girl" tape. I wondered which one it was. I only knew the difference if he told me because their songs, to me, sounded the same. Yet Elliott knew every nuance of each song and sang them accordingly. I admired that a bit. No matter the song, he would always catch the words in the song, head lowered, singing them softly and off-key, his fingers wrapped listlessly around one or two dreads. I was never carried away like that with music. I loved music but I also liked the hear just sounds of the city, like the faint roar of wind rushing in my ear as I drive along Lincoln Boulevard toward the 10 Freeway.

"I liked that place," Elliott said, his eyes catching mine, as he turned to focus them on the street. "That little Italian place. I think the name of it is..."

"Granitti's," I said. "Too much food," I added, remembering how much tortellini in white sauce had covered my plate. Elliott's turn to pick a restaurant had come up and he had chosen it after reading the *L.A. Weekly's* "Pick of the Week." Settled into the basement of a sweatshop, it was a thin, long restaurant with only enough room to have a row of tables on each side. Blinding white walls, covered with rusted junk that hovered above each table like broken umbrellas, coupling with the dark and funky ambiance that permeated smoky gray tables, walls clashing with frigid red-and-white gingham checked plastic tablecloths that acted as shields under the orchestrated noise of clattering plates, while vacuous actors, moonlighting as waiters, mumbled, "I'll never have to do this shit again," as they strode toward the kitchen to pick up the table's next entree, counting their tips without a hand leaving the apron's pocket, serving large stiff drinks and food that rose high as mountains threatening to spill over glass placemats of Norman Rockwell drawings which anchored cheap red candleholders, their flames dancing upon Elliott's glasses. That's what I remember about Granitti's. We argued there. Another time I think the real and emotional Elliott had come through. Still, the bitterness of that night rankles my own emotions. Surprise would be an understatement, but it was a moment when I fully realized what Elliott meant to be black.

I drove down Lincoln Boulevard which seemed like a ghost town at 11:00 p.m. I glanced at Elliott out of the corner of my eye, while reaching up to adjust the back mirror. Just a move to fill up space. I really didn't need to because driving a convertible allows you to see everything, sans a window. Images of that night knocked quietly on my door of memories.

"Why?" Elliott asked, stuffing chicken and garlic pasta into his mouth, his almond shaped eyes locking with mine.

"Because I think they, black women," I said, correcting myself, "are so powerful..."

"What do you mean, 'they' he said, resting his fork on top of his plate. "You're black, too, you know. Maybe not as much as I have, because one thing about me brother, I'm black. Every time you talk about black people you talk about it like it's a 'us' thing. Not a 'you' thing. You want to forget you're half, huh?"

"I'm not saying that," I said, picking up my water glass to take a drink. "You're always viewing my comments, or anyone's, in some paranoid racist perspective."

"And I have every right to do so," Elliott said, his eyes, darkened by rage, smoldered.

"You don't have my right," I shot back, nervously pulling at my ponytail. "I wish you would stop trying to appropriate my feelings about everything."

"You're missing the point again. You should already know about half of what I mean," Elliott said, continuing to fork food into his mouth.

"Because I'm mulatto, I'm supposed to know what black men feel like?"

"Being raised by white parents, I'm sure, is going to erase quite a bit of black history from your life, but you can't even do a fucking reality check about who you are. If I didn't know you I would think that you're this quasi-Latino teacher, the way you hang out with your students and their families," Elliott said.

"What's wrong with that? I'm the soccer coach. I'm supposed to do that. Half the team is in my class," I said angrily.

"For the last month I haven't seen you more than three times a week. Soccer practice. Soccer pizza. Soccer family night. Do you have to spend twenty-four hours with them?" Elliott said, playing with his food with his fork. "Isn't it enough that you're bilingual? Hell, anytime I'm there with you, you speak Spanish like I'm some tourist on vacation."

"Most of them don't know good English," I said, quietly fuming inside.

"Teach them English: you practically do everything else," Elliott said.

"I'm doing that already," I said quickly, hoping that we would talk about something else. Almost half the time I had been seeing Peter. Soccer was the perfect excuse for tardiness.

"Come on sweetheart," I said, touching Elliott's hand, "let's not argue tonight, let's just enjoy the food." I had spoken so softly that I knew he had strained to hear me.

"You always say that," he said, picking up a piece of bread. He never raised his eyes as he buttered it, saying, "Yeah, I guess you're right. I'm being the angry black man again. Time to pull me off stage with the hook."

"Stop being so dramatic or I'll start calling you Mr. Bojangles," I said, laughing at my joke, before I picked up my wine glass to stifle my giggles.

"Fuck you, Mr. Homogenization."

I set down my wine glass and began toying with my tortellini, now cold and stiff. I had crossed the line. Elliott hated joking about historical black icons.

"Regardless of the stereotypes they portrayed, these black men and women were the foundation of black performers today. Now they're regarded as some derisive caricatures of the shiftless nigger, which the media perpetuates," he said once at a recent party we'd gone to where the subject had turned to why today's black generation shunned the historical perspective Hattie McDaniel, Butterfly McQueen, Amos n' Andy and the Nicholas Brothers provided.

Elliott said nothing. We ate in silence, bits of inconsequential conversation lazily stumbling from our mouths, a combined effort to appear cordial. I watched him out of the corner of my eye and glanced at the passing waiter. Across from me sat a man who wouldn't even watch "In Living Color" because he believed that it was simply the continuation of stereotypical myths about blacks, permeating to a higher degree, he said, in the white suburbs where it aired.

"Hey baby," I heard Elliott say, his eyes lowered sideways, watching me. "Sometimes I get too emotional about being black, I know that. Then again, sometimes I have to do so. Maybe it's because every time I see the homeless people or just bums on the street, here, New York, Chicago, San Francisco, man, they're all black! That's why I keep my anger here," he said, patting his chest.

"I feel that, sometimes, you vent that out on me, unfairly," I said. "I'm not the cause of this and if I want to look past it, that's my right too. I'm just Larry."

"I know."

I pulled into the turning lane for the 10 Freeway, headed towards downtown. That was the fastest way to get home. I watched as the smoke from Elliott's cigarette disappeared into the air. I shifted the car into third gear as I followed a rusted Dodge van onto the freeway. As soon as I could get the chance, I was going to pull ahead of it. Now in fourth gear, I looked into the side mirror and pulled into the next lane. I liked driving in the right lanes on the freeway. I stayed behind a new Nissan Maxima until I came to the La Cienega exit, using the curve to glide behind a lumbering Range Rover which whizzed by. I looked over at Elliott as he tossed his cigarette out. In the rearview mirror I saw the ashes hit the pavement like small firecrackers before the next car's gust blew it out. I gazed over at the center of Los Angeles, the lights scattered into infinity. This city never seemed to end, I thought, as I was wondered just where this relationship, our relationship was headed. Was it over? I read the signs that pointed to Crenshaw and Arlington. Just how many times have I driven past these signs in the twenty-six years that I've lived here? I knew Los Angeles. It was funny, what people thought about it, what they were expecting, when they moved here. They came, expecting Los Angeles to be this real city. It was real and it wasn't real. Angelenos, like myself, knew the difference. They didn't. It was too hard to explain, just a feeling that we all inherited, learning to move in the perpetually golden tunnel vision that draped the chessboard Los Angeles lay upon. I slowed down a bit as I neared the ramp that merged with the Hollywood Freeway, easing into the right lane as I followed the line of blinking red lights which reminded me of the plastic peppers that hung in one of the Mexican restaurants in East Los Angeles. I remembered the first time that Elliott had taken me there. "The only place to have real Mexican food," he had said. Again, he was right. His ability to find these places irked me. I was the one who spoke Spanish.

"Do you want to stop anywhere?" I asked Elliott as we merged onto the freeway. I drove past the Alvarado and Echo Park exits toward the Silverlake exit before he answered.

"No. I don't need to stop anywhere."

Elliott lit a cigarette as I waited to turn onto Silverlake Boulevard. I watched him as he took a drag and turned his head to blow it out.

"Hey," he said.

"Hey, what, dude?" I said, as I held the side of Elliott's seat while I drove.

"How ya feelin?"

That was our catch phrase for it's-time-to-talk. And this time I said nothing. I imagined sentences reeling in my head like home movies, only to disappear once my lips began to form the words. I slowed down to make a left hand turn onto Berkeley Avenue. I inched up the road in second gear, cars lined up on both sides of the street, hugging the sidewalks like lovers. I drove past Effie Street, catching a glimpse of my former apartment before Elliott and I had moved in together.

"I'm not sure how I feel," I said as the car crept up the hill. At the crest of it stood our apartment. The street leveled out where we lived. A nice touch that made our cars feel lucky, their brakes were never strained.

"I'm feeling a lot of different things myself," Elliott said, his dreads shielding his face.

"Like what?" I said, lifting up some of his dreads with my fingers.

"Where we're at, our relationship, now that you've slept with Peter."

"Elliott, I love you. It's not that big of a deal. I just slept with him, once. We should just try to work things out from here," I said, turning the engine off and pulling up the emergency brake.

"It is a big deal, Larry, with me. We never discussed it and I have a strange feeling that this has probably been going on for a while."

I shifted in my seat, leaning back to stretch my legs. I put my hand on Elliott's shoulder, pressing him toward me.

"I love you so much," he said, as he turned toward me. "Our current, this feeling I share with you, it's interrupted by this debris I know nothing about. Something's changed and it's not me."

"I didn't think you were going to react this way," I said.

"How did you think that I was going to react?" Elliott said, straightening up and shifting sideways, allowing light to reflect on the black vinyl seat.

"I thought you would get angry, cry and then we move on from here," I said, watching car headlights approaching us, outlining Elliott's bug. He didn't speak until the car had passed.

"You're still not able to see the gray areas, are you?" Elliott asked, lighting another cigarette. He took a drag and continued. "Categorizing my emotions, I never used to see that. A part of me was so in love with you. I felt I had to be everything you wanted me to be. However, through this groove, my own identity as a proud black gay man was taking second place to yours."

"You were too passive in our relationship when things affected me," I said, tracing designs over the steering wheel with my fingers. "There were so many times that I wanted to tell you that."

"Why didn't you?" Elliott asked, blowing the smoke, his eyes staring at the sky. "You're right; at times, I was passive because I didn't want to experience any of your moods. I think at first that I enjoyed it, being able, at least I thought, to wipe away your bad feelings, showing you other ones. I forgot my own."

"Do you think that we could work on it," I said, my voice a bit unsteady as I turned off the question part of it. Breaking up with Elliott was going to be much easier. "I don't want to lose you."

"You lost me even before Peter," Elliott said, his hand moving across my chin, around and under it, turning my face toward his. "I love you and I always will, but I feel that even if we work on it, our relationship would only fall back into the same rut."

"That's not true," I said, placing my fingers over Elliott's fingers as they cradled the emergency brake. "We can try. Okay, dude?"

"I'm not one of your fucking students. Stop patronizing me. I don't feel like trying anymore," he said, taking his hand away from my face. "You're right, this has more to do with just sleeping with Peter."

"What do you mean by that?" I asked, staring straight ahead.

"Tell me something," Elliott asked quietly, almost hesitating, "This affair you've had with Peter is still going on, isn't it?"

"No, it's over," I said, stumbling over the last syllables. "It was just a one-night deal."

"And when you see him," Elliott said, looking directly into my eyes, "You guys don't have sex."

"I told you the answer a second ago. It's still no," I said.

"I don't think you really know me. Sometimes when I hear you talk to me or any of your other friends about our relationship it seems I'm some sort of study and the only reason that we're in this relationship is because I'm black. You don't look at me like I'm me, Elliott."

"That's unfair, dude," I said softly. Yet it wasn't. I knew that. When Elliott and I began dating I had never dated a black man before. Our honeymoon period was great, but as time passed I began to see parts of the racism that Elliott talked about so much. It was true. Sometimes when we went out, very few white guys would come up and talk to me. The terror of being labeled a dinge queen was something I couldn't bear. Knowing that I was mixed made me want to shout, "But I'm half-white!" on those occasions and sometimes I would actually tell them. Black history was something that my adopted parents never considered and I see their intentions behind it. I was never really aware of what it really meant to be black, live as a black man, but I knew swatches of the experience. Yet, my feelings for Elliott were genuine and any superficial interest had certainly waned in the early weeks of our relationship.

"On whose part?" he asked, raising up and crossing his legs near his feet.

"If you feel that the only reason that we're together is because you are black then perhaps you're right in that we should call it quits. I can always find another black man," I said, pushing the lever to move the seat back. "Shouldn't we go in," I asked, opening the car door. "It's cold out here."

"It's amazing," Elliott said, his face staring straight ahead, "how in just a few minutes you can realize everything you never wanted to know about someone, that it's real and true, something that you didn't want to see. I saw that in you tonight."

"Let's go inside, dude," I said, buttoning up my jacket.

"No, let's stay outside a few more moments," Elliott said, stuffing his hands in his pockets. "We always seem to talk better in the car."

"And why is that, dude?" I asked, pulling my hair into a loose knot. While I waited for Elliott to answer, I admitted, we did have our best conversations in the car. During our relationship we always tried to resolve things before we actually went inside our house. Yet this time, straining my eyes to catch stars in the sky, maybe this wouldn't be resolved.

"I feel safe talking to you now," Elliott said, "But I know you're getting agitated because you've called me "dude" almost five times and it's starting to sound sarcastic. Yet I know that if I was inside that house I would be reminded of how much I love you. I just don't know babe."

Suddenly, Elliott turned toward me, grabbed my head, his fingers covered with my hair, now loose and hanging, and shouted "Why?" His scream echoed from the hilltop and slammed against the palm trees that shaded our house, rolling down the hill until it rested at the foot of Sunset Boulevard. His hands, molded to my face, began caressing my eyes and lips. I breathed deeply, struggling to regain my composure. His voice, guttural and hard like the sound of gravel being crunched, drifted toward me, circling around my ears as he kept repeating, "Why?" I watched his Adam's apple rise and fall, rise and fall, rise and fall, the word silently dropping from his lips.

And for the second time that night, words escaped hollow and lifeless from my mouth as they ricocheted in my mind, falling flat against my vocal chords. I felt Elliott's hands fall from my face. I watched the shadow of his fingers in the darkness of the car, balled into sepia fists, open and close with each passing second. I'm sorry, I wanted to say to him but I knew that I couldn't. I turned away from Elliott and stared across the street in the gated sloping yards, rocks and cacti lined up like borders, jutting delicately into the night air, my elbow hanging over the door, chin cupped in my hand. I had left us long ago. My fingers traced upon the cracked one-inch dashboard as I thought of how I might find myself at Peter's, tonight.

Elliott got out of the car a few seconds later. "This drive is over," he said, leaning over the window. I watched him walk towards the door of our house. I waited to cry when I heard the door close.

Dope

Using dope has become a common thing
In spite of the misery it brings.
It substitutes falsehood for truth,
It's the number one enemy of our youth.
It bankrupts the store house of your soul
And renders your spirit Arctic cold.
It glamorizes and disguises the horrors of its grip
While it rules you and even fools you into thinking you are hip.
Its candy coated poison, too,
A death trap; a snare for you.
Anything that robs you of hope
Can be categorized along with dope.

Dope is a cancer that's self induced
A relentless foe on the loose,
An evil, evil thing I say;
There is no time for us to play.
It robs you of your self control
It enslaves heart, body, mind and soul.
Its strange sensations takes your will,
Its an evil thing designed to kill.

A sneak attack has surely been sprung
By diabolical forces that kill OUR YOUNG.
Its COCAINE parading as a ray of hope
For fragmented minds unwilling to cope.
Like a minute parading as an HOUR,
A GAS CHAMBER parading as a SHOWER.

But the time has come to show and tell,
The story of dope, the living hell.
An EVIL disguised as good
It must be exposed and understood.
It's a back-stabber smiling in your face,
It respects no color, class, or race.
Dope steals the laughter of your years
And grieves your spirit with CRIMSON tears.
It will confuse and vex a solid mind,
It will never show the bottom line.

Dope is the hideous queen and hideous bride,
Of a hideous crime called GENOCIDE.
It's a holocaust second to none
More devastating than an atomic bomb.
This merciless killer controls your streets
It even dares you to stand on your feet.
But breaking the yoke of this EVIL BAND
Bbegins by our first taking a STAND.
For the victims of DOPE are both YOU and I
If we just sit idly by
And WATCH OUR CHILDREN suffer & DIE.

Monday

water broke
monday
missie beth like to have
a fit all over her new floor she say
i to wipe up what i done
and get over there by the backdoor

she mad
'cause of in the pantry
mr. sam he
take down my panties

big mama would know
i seen her
when other womens come
to be under her hands
stomachs swelled like too full cotton
sacks begging her empty them
give back the peace

this one ain't fighting
maybe i having a angel
a baby jesus
out of my own stomach

at last he come
and i hardly knew
i pick he off the cold
floor and pinch he leg
like big mama do

she say
only reason white man hit
they babies is so they get mean
spirited like bad ghosts
always looking to hit
back

he ain't cried once
missie beth say he dead
and call charlie yard man
take him out

i please her let me
show him big mama
i please her give me some
things to wash him

but she say he dead
and charlie come
i take off he cord
and charlie wrap he
in a brown burlap sack

missie beth tell me
check the pots
and the meat
when she gone

i put he cord in they
nice dinner soup

From This Generation On

I remember my great grandmother with long gray hair parted in the middle and braided atop her head; Indian-like features—high cheek bones, well defined chin, deep brown skin, slightly wrinkled—corncob pipe in the corner of her mouth; fiery, cold, piercing eyes when angry; long fingers clutched into a tight fist waving menacingly into the air; always eighty.

I remember her passion, her possessiveness, her strength, her matriarchal control. I remember her toothless frowns, her sweet smell of tobacco, her touch, her voice—high pitched and cracked—her stories, her stories about my roots that at the time I ignored but now long to remember. I was twelve; she was eighty-four—sitting in her rocking chair, rocking, rocking—and then no more.

I remember my grandmother-strong, supportive, head of the family, making all the decisions, knowing everything, proud, stalwart in her ways and refusing to change. I remember her round body, "high yellow" complexion and warm smile. I remember a woman who loved me like her own, filled with humility and righteousness; believing and instilling in me that God and education were everything in life; a woman who taught school for forty-nine-and-a-half years, dedicating her life to her career and then at age sixty-five was forced to retire; a woman who began a slow decline but fought it bravely.

I remember her last year in and out of the hospital, struggling with stiffening limbs, failing organs, and mental deterioration. I remember her gallant fight to do the things that used to be so natural to her, reading her bible and the newspaper daily but no longer able to remember what she'd read; trying to maintain her independence and dignity but forced to succumb to helplessness and humiliation; and finally writing her own obituary.

I was a young lady with a baby growing deep within me; a child that she would never know but would have loved the way I do. She was an inspiration, a memory to be forever cherished—gone but not forgotten.

I remember my mother when she first lost her own, becoming dependent on me but gaining strength everyday, growing more and more like her mother and grandmother, yet she is different in many ways. There's still the fire, but an endearing warmth comes forth. There's still the dominance but also an acknowledgment that I am now an adult, too. There's still the independence which I will always admire. There's still the love that will never die.

Being the fourth generation of daughters, I realize as I see the circle complete itself that we are all extensions of our mothers. No matter how different we feel or want to be, there are innate qualities that endure and connect us from generation to generation. The qualities of inner strength, independence, and perseverance, I eagerly embrace, for with age comes wisdom and understanding. I now understand the importance of all my great grandmother's magnificent stories, the wisdom behind my grandmother's advice, "Be strong and be smart," and the meaning of my mother's reminder, "Don't forget your roots." I feel a common bond with all black mothers who have struggled and succeeded in life, for it was through the voices of our mothers that we became what we are.

My daughter is the fifth generation. I wonder how she will remember me.

Any Day Now

Blues,
Blacks,
Browns,
Greens,
blend into the cracked earth,
Into the broken glass
And abandoned buildings,
Into fenced-in playgrounds
With dirty needles,
And hoops with
No nets.
Black faces with empty eyes
And concrete skin,
Puffy black hands hold
Brown paper bags,
(hold it tight)
Brown paper bags,
(hold it tight)
Hold themselves,
(hold it tight)
Down.

1940's

What's up Gates? i am negro chicago's 1940's in my time of racial segregation i longed for better jobs better homes & a better way of life the question of negro cultural awareness in my era was never answered i was too involved in the hunger for survival the negroes of my era felt they were getting better jobs when in reality they were getting dirtylowpayingstockyardstillmillass j-o-bs Ain't That a Blip! all of this was a result of world war II because the whites were shipping out to serve their country which served them so well negroes became passive to overt racism such as the jim crow laws negroes were not given the opportunity to compete educationally they were rejected from predominantly white colleges like depaul roosevelt & northwestern Be cool Be cooool! the negroes of my era were advised to keep cool and avoid confrontations with whites the whole mentality of my era was segregation and separation even though i had the blues i didn't let the blues overtake my body and soul the song and dance of my era expressed my ability to keep on movin' no matter what jazz jazzzzzz i expressed my joy my sorrow count bassie billie holliday ethyl waters marva lewis earl "father" hynes duke ellington chick webb ella fitzgerald buck clayton lester young kenneth korsey...Boy Were Those Some Kool Cats! jam sessions at the civic opera and joint hoppin' all night those were the days 47th south parkway was the center of my world the savoy ballroom grand terrace club delisa rrrrrum boogie parkway ballroom & who could forget the regal a night on the town consisted of a ride on "the big red" couldn't afford a car 50 cents would get you and a date into the regal for a movie and a stage show $1.50 bought two dinners at morrie's eats on 47th then we'd hit the 708 club for some blues even aunt jemima was alive and well...throwing parties all the time we told the whites Stop Misbusin' Me! but our voices weren't loud enough so instead we sang the blues...and let the trumpet

w

h

i

n

e

A Thank You Note

Dear Officer Falk:

I want to thank you for your care and the thoughtful manner in which you performed your job in the incident, last Friday, involving my son, Brian Welch.

I am sure you were quite concerned each and every time that Brian was reported in a inappropriate area and dangerous predicament.

I am probably noted in this town as an incompetent parent. I wondered if I could give you a brief history of Brian's social life.

Born March 14, 1982, he was what some doctors call colicky, meaning he cried hours at a time. He had this condition for a much longer period than some babies. He began to try to walk at 9 months, but I never noticed a recognizable syllable until well after.

At 2-3 years old, he did have a stay in the hospi tal after being grazed by an old lady in the parking lot across the street from Pomona Valley Hospital. By then his speech development was noticeably defi cient. However, when, for instance, we went to a public place where we had to just sit and listen, Brian was disruptive of the proceedings.

I tried not to let this ruin my social life but after being made an example of, over and over, by age 5, we (Brian had a brother, Jeremy) could no longer at tend 2-3 hour services. I was labeled a no-account mom who couldn't discipline her children. Thereaf ter, I developed and nurtured phobias of closed-in spaces.

Whenever we went to the doctor, they noted that his iron level was always too low. As I reflect on that period, Brian was a runner and that's about all he did at times. He had an interest in learning but he wasn't picking up words. Jeremy was a God-sent because, before him, I had nothing to measure Brian's cogni tive and social development by.

His only response to a word was to repeat it as you said it. (If you're wondering if I've ever taken il legal drugs, I assure you that the shoe doesn't fit on my foot.)

I wanted Brian to get some kind of treatment, so I was referred to SGV Regional Center by Mary Hig gins, the principal of El Camino. The tested him and concluded that he was not especially qualified for their services, in 1989. I mentioned his hyperactivity and they said he could grow out of it and that Ritalin, a drug prescribed to ease hyperac tivity, was very ex perimental.

Did I feel discriminated against because I was poor and an Afro-American single parent? Yes.

Meanwhile, Brian got a very bad case of Chicken Pox from his brother. Every subsequent year, he would get strep throat and bronchial colds. He was a walking germ magnet.

At age 9, Brian started resisting going to the clinic for medication. He resisted going in the market, as well. He didn't even want to go to Disneyland with us, but there was a big crowd and I held onto his hand.

I can hear your mind's wheels turning: You're thinking that Mom just doesn't exert enough influ ence on her kid(s) and she'd probably benefit from some parental counseling. That could be true but it isn't.

I caution you against such placing of blame as there are many things that appear to be one way on the surface, but a more intelligent person looks deeper than that.

Again, I praise you for your careful analysis of the situation. You did the right thing in placing my son in a foster care home.

Maybe if I could explain the history of Brian's education, that would be helpful to you.

When we lived in the Pomona School District, Brian was branded the most misbehaved kid in the land. His attendance at Barfield lasted a total of about two weeks. He was then bussed to Kingsley and then, Alcott, all in his kindergarten year. Brian stole the scene everywhere he went. He was boisterous, disruptive, and squarely against any edu cational program. Who was more reprehensible the parent or the child, was not the issue. The issue was how to make Brian sit in his seat, how to make Brian pay attention to instruction, and how to make Brian stop making those weird, moaning sounds (instead of comprehensible words).

Somewhere between first and second grade, he was transferred to El Camino, a school for kids with handicaps and, most notably, birth defects. I think we all felt the undesirable sting of that move. I had to admit that the School District had its hands tied be cause Brian's behavior was very volatile at times.

I felt the sting because I had always represented just the opposite in my childhood and throughout my academic life. I attended ULV on a scholarship the first year and worked my way, paying the tuition with government grants, loans, and my own earnings, as an Office Clerk.

After he was out for six weeks with Chicken Pox, he was transferred to Yorba. Yorba, like all the schools Brian had attended, had the same complaint, i.e., Brian would seem perfectly content sometimes but he had serious mood swings. He made impulsive and self-endangering moves. He was scene stealer. He required a constant guardian.

He was being referred to as a high-functioning Autistic Child with some normal tendencies. I be came accustomed to hearing these terms, used only in circles with Master's and Ph.D. in Education. It hurt my feelings and, of course, I felt inadequate. I have a B.A. in Journalism but I, jokingly, think that I deserve an honorary degree in Child Psychology.

I decided that Brian was being ostracized by the busing to Pomona (we moved to Claremont when he was 6). At 9 years of age, I asked that he be moved to a Mountain View Class for kids with slow language development or Aphasia.

When that class was discontinued the following year, due to budget constraints, he was transferred to Danbury, another school for the physically handi capped.

There was nothing I could do about getting Brian out of these types of schools, even though I felt in my heart, that it affected his self-esteem. My worst fear is that if I had more resources and assistance from the health care industry, could things have been more specialized for him and me?

Maybe a private school would have been better? Why was I not qualified for any of the services of the Regional Center, when all the educators told me otherwise?

I kept hearing, all along, that there are so many kinds that are hyperactive, like Brian. I wanted to explore that possibility by attending conferences held in places such as, Irvine and West Los Angeles. Usu ally I couldn't make arrangements to attend because either the costs were prohibitive or I didn't have adequate transportation. I did notice that child care was provided. (I'm a welfare recipient and, like so many others, my closest blood relative is about an hour's drive away.

This year when Brian started taking off to far off places on his bike (a Christmas gift from me), I was, admittedly, alarmed. When he started walking to the railroad tracks, which are about a block east and a block north of the apartment complex, I was some times at work and sometimes not..you know the story. I don't have a job anymore, incidentally.

Now, my main concern is that Brian receive the psychological evaluation and that he have some kind of trial pharmaceutical treatment. There is a lot of hope, in this respect, because he's never been assessed as a candidate for behavior modification therapy.

Again, thank you for your support and crisis intervention.

Sincerely,
Brian's Anonymous Mother

Go Life

When I was a slave
You took my children away from me
For your own profit.

Now you tell me,
Go Pro Life!

When I sent my child to be
Schooled with yours,
You humiliated him and
Denied him his Constitutional Right —
To receive a free public education.
You excluded him and ridiculed him
Based on the color of his skin.

Now you tell me,
Go Pro Life!

You sterilized me and my sisters
Against our will
So we might not infest your
Cotton white world with
Beautiful Black Babies.

Now you tell me,
Go Pro Life!

You make it difficult for my
Stable Brothers and Sisters to adopt
Many unwanted children alive now—
Though they are
Sound, sane and, financially—able
And willing to ease the
Horrid conditions of foster care.

You tell us all,
Vote Pro Life!

True Irony:
If I produce another beautiful Black child,
Will you give him true life?

Will you give him an equal chance
To acquire an equal, not separate
Education so that he might
Become a valuable member of this society?

Will you give him life?
Will you fairly assess his qualifications
For your next employment opportunity
In which he is fully capable of mastering?

Are you still pro life?

When he has acquired funds to
Move in your neighborhood,
Attend your social functions—date your daughter
Will you acknowledge him as a life you saved from oblivion?

Or, will your institutions
Chide him and tell him
He is not qualified for your loan?
Deny him the "privilege" to shop in your stores,
Perhaps, harass him because he happens
To drive an expensive car through your community.

Compatriot,
Your issue has no validity to me.
It serves as a political farce
That perpetuates your feeble point-of-view,
Based on a historical mound of
Wretched points-of-view.

I don't believe
You are truly Pro Life!

Speed

It is six am and this is how some people waste money: They get a hotel room so they don't have to drive home. The blond hair promises everything and robs me of expectation. How can I ever be anything without weighing one-zero-eight and having blond hair? I am glad when the instructor, a real writer, a brunette, tells Miss Clairol that her three pages "could have been faxed in from anywhere." She will not last in this cutthroat class.

I have never been her size and that is my trouble. She is blond and so doesn't know trouble. Isn't that what the movies tell us? I, however, will not disgrace myself as blond. I have wanted to be a hundred things, but blond fits me like shoes on Masai warriors' feet. I hate her because she has money.

I have driven here from Irvine, never considering a hotel room, and know the 405 like the back of my hand. The cities fly by as I hurry to be on time. What she misses is this: driving at 85. There is no traffic when you get on in Irvine. Costa Mesa fades into Fountain Valley, you don't remember Westminster 'til you are through it, and when Seal Beach Boulevard shows up on the sign you know you're almost to the border.

You wait for the twenty-two as you pass Studebaker, Cherry, Avocado. You are in a hurry as you fly because this is the first time you have breathed and you know that soon they will come short. It is like sweet wine on an empty stomach: You are high and then you are asleep.

You keep your eyes open for the wacked highway patrol. You are speeding and you know that their job is seditious. Stopping the flow of anything is unnatural. Beating someone senseless is the only logical next step.

The carpool lane ends and there is no more eighty-five, there is just seventy. Reduction of speed is the end of illusion. Blond hair rules. You remember being a child who could never run; you chased someone only twice in your life. Weight buoyed you down like that Masai warrior's shoes. You read books instead, focused on being smart, didn't mind the other kids hating you. You were in pursuit of something rare, knowing even then that blond hair could never be yours. You have to get in a car to fly and that is why you speed.

You are always chasing something. You have lived so many thin lives and you have written none of them. Your inhalation is labored and you want them to understand, the rest of the class, Miss Clairol, that a few steps is all you can take before your breath is cut off. You feel how an asthmatic's zephyr becomes a sirocco.

That is why you fly on freeways. Speed is how you live. Catatonic nights beginning with Mrs. Fields cookies over you have learned what the fast lane is like and like it. You will ask married Mordecai for a kiss yet.

It is your turn. The real writer points to you. Last night's words flow back.

Eating yourself to death is not pretty, you read. That is part of the calm of the midnight hours-you can look at yourself and not see the bulk...

(They interrupt to say you are reading too fast. You begin again, not wanting this to be excruciating but seeing no way to avoid it.)

...can walk nations without hearing the slap of skin. You don't know that relief; your fat hounds you like a nightmare on roller skates.

You don't really want to die anymore, you tell them, not like those nights on half a dozen Mrs. Field's and two dinners. All you really wanted was the invisibility your weight afforded you. No one took you seriously at three hundred pounds. You could be whatever, say don't drop bombs at an awards dinner and no one would really listen because it was a fat woman saying it and everyone knew you just laughed at fat people and suggested the latest good diet. No one had done that in this class, you remind them, but then they are all writers and what do they know.

Following the assignment, you tell them you write because there is intense sanity in it. It is the only time your schizophrenia is an advantage. It is when you can let the voices within you speak; it is where you can let your frailties show and never be ashamed. It is where you can kill your family with impunity.

Sounds the instructor asked for; you'll give her sounds. You tell her about the sound of a forbidden chocolate chip cookie going down your throat at ten miles per hour—one doesn't speed with chocolate— and it is the smile afterwards that speaks. But you are rambling; you will give them the already perfect words that you shared at the awards banquet last night.

You have defied the instructor and not canceled your plans for Saturday evening. They asked you to speak and you will not disappoint them. The instructor has asked you to write about an hour in time and you decide to tell her about seven o'clock when you were standing at the podium reading your words to a very polite audience. You give her those words from another story, words you do not expect this cutthroat instructor to say are better as prose:

i am sorry artemio
for thinking venezuela is a one horse town
but that is all i was taught of south america

you see i, a young black child, i always got a's
was always teacher's pet
safe in the hatred of the other children
because i was so bright
got to college thinking the one horse towns started at mexico

i am sorry artemio
for looking into that textbook you assigned me
and for being stunned by the description of thriving cities in
    venezuela
i apologize for the poor characters in my novel wearing
    "native "dress
a dress i could not even describe

you faced me with my own racism
and i, in my brilliant ignorance did not recognize it
i will add to this apology, beloved artemio
your silence as you waited for me to recognize limits

i add to this image
your being taken away by military policemen
for having books on cubism
they thought they were books on cuba

i understand, beloved artemio
why you left the university
that i, a black woman, victim in my own right
could be so blind

how that must have hurt you
must have angered you
and now, artemio, now
i know enough to be angry too

You are flushed and then worried reciting them. Will they see
your sorrow for a gifted professor who gave up teaching? Will they
know how many hours you spent in his office, how you agonized over

passing his classes, how you did so just barely never sure you had his approval and knowing at the last you didn't? You are positive they know nothing and hope they see it all.

It is almost over. You read the last paragraph of the three page assignment and wait for the real writer to speak. She does, true to her nature. "The good, the bad, and the indifferent," she says. "This is not poetry; it is deformed prose." You are crushed. You wanted to be the best and you are not. You do not look at Miss Clairol.

You busy yourself taking notes on the real writer's furious comments. She is speaking quickly, there are ten more assignments to get through and class is almost over. In the end you only cared that what you wrote was good, but this was not your best effort and you knew it. You remember the polite applause at the awards banquet and the real writer's premonition that no accolades are worth the loneliness and pulling out from self that is writing.

The criticism is over. Your turn has come and gone and you are still alive. You look at the real writer and at blond hair and know that there will be other times, other classes. Most of all you know that the freeway, and breathlessness, is waiting. You will go eighty-five again before you die and that is all that counts.

Untitled

(for tony anderson, on his twenty-ninth birthday)

warm soft negro folds of skin
skin melting warm in closeness
skin damp with the wetness of tears
arms enfolding
embracing beyond skin to soul
skin reaching deep
touching bone
massaging emotional pain
scarring old childhood wounds
arms forever open
forever consoling
smile teaching me to smile
at that frightened broken child
down below

child sat
waiting
all car engines
melting into that one car engine
she was a girl
but knew the particular purr
that carried her father to her
car engines melting
that purr—yes!—then, no, not that purr
sinking again into the folds of that couch
mother's couch
child
waiting

he never came

night and day again
the explanatory phone call
gambling again
night and day then afternoon
he comes
she laughs
buries the hurt the wait
under miles of:
where have i failed him?
what have i done again to cause the wait?
but buries it in a corner of
mother's couch
smiles, laughs, is gay
only wonders
what the hair is on her head
that defect in her soul
making the wait
a necessity

she waits
to be reassured
she is loved

it never comes

at thirty-five she is perennially late to work
she is waiting
they have told her once
your work is excellent
we are grateful
be on time
one month later
perennially late
she waits for the ax

it does not come

she waits to be reassured
to be told she is valued
to be loved

it does not come

she goes back to that couch
digs up that hurt
cleaves it to her skin
feeds it to the child suffocating down below
brings her up for air
is not late again

she knows it will not come

the skin though is there
the negro folds of skin
enfolding
an embrace no lighter shade knows
an embrace no lighter shade needs
an embrace dusky and smelly
an embrace old as chains
old as master rape
old as middle passage
an embrace only we could create for each other
an embrace born of the dusk of our skin
as we landed on this hell america
it saves her now
it is a receptacle for the salt tea of tears
it absorbs the wetness into the skin
and makes heat of it
a fever that burns the pain out
there is no sex here
only what the child who sat
who waited
waited for

Hard Miles to Four Miles

The neighbor's clothes still smelled of sweat and creosote from packing railroad ties at the tie plant, and his face was grim as he relayed to Mama what he had heard at work. Aunt Butch's words, carried by three or four different men, traveling through the grapevine across two counties, had reached their destination. I could not hear all they were saying, but I was old enough to know that the message about Grandma was serious.

"Ma's sick. Come!"

The man shuffled away, and mumbled slowly, "I tried to git you a ride, Bill, but couldn't."

The sun hung low in the sky, and Papa and my brothers were still in the field. Mama finished supper, then went to the back door and yelled to our nearest neighbor.

"Sarah, I'm goin' to Ma's. She's sick. I'm sending Dolores up there till Sam comes. My little sucker I'm taking with me."

My sister ran up the hill and Mama squatted down and told me to get on her back. I put my arms around her neck, and she locked her arms under my legs and took off down the road in a trot.

"We gonna cut through the thickets 'cause I want to get through Yegua Bottom 'fore dark," she said.

On and on we went. My arms and legs were tired. I wondered if Mama was tired, but we kept going. For me as a child, she was like an old sow with a runt on her back.

Night was falling as we crossed the creaky, old iron bridge at Yegua Creek, and I could barely see the Indian writing on the trees. Mama had said that when the white men were running the Indians out of the area, the Indians threw their gold in the creek and hollered 'Yegua' and that was how the creek got its name. Anyway, once we crossed the bridge, we were out of Burleson County and into Washington County.

Mama's pace slowed when she saw a dimly lit house through the woods. With me still on her back she knocked on the door. A man with a worried voice answered, "Who is it?"

"Bill!" Mama yelled.

"Bill?" The man shouted as he opened the door. "You know better than to be out with that gal this time of night."

"I'm going to Ma's and I want you to take me!"

"You go no farther tonight! Come in and eat somethin'. I'll get up and take you early in the morning." The man was dark and pot-bellied. His wife was light-skinned and had a pretty smile.

After a little supper the man's wife gave me a wash pan and water to wash my feet. I wanted to listen to what they were talking about because they sounded like old friends, but before long I had snuggled into the feather mattress and was fast asleep. Later I learned they were kin and had gone to school with Mama.

It seemed like only minutes and it was time to get up. Everything looked different in daylight. The couple's house had brick siding, not old gray, weathered boards like ours. They had a nice garden, lots of chicken and hogs, but no children.

Mama was up early and ready to go. We ate a little breakfast and then climbed into the man's black Model A Ford and were on our way again.

I remember crossing the bridge at Four Miles. It was my favorite creek, prettier than the old muddy Yegua. Four Miles' water was always clean and running. Its bottom had holes like old lace, and was scattered with rocks and white sand. After crossing Four Miles we were in Lee County and closer to Grandma's.

When we passed Saint Mary's Church Mama smiled a little. I guess she was thinking like Br'er Rabbit after his tail was pulled off, "It ain't long no more now."

Across the road was Grandpa's property. The man stopped the car and got out to open the big gate. He drove through, closed the gate, and down the road we went.

The Model A came to a quick stop in front of Grandpa's. When Aunt Butch saw Mama, she ran back in the house screaming, "Bill's here, Ma! Bill's here."

Grandpa came out leaning on his cane. He was tall, tan, and wore a wide black hat. Looking down on me he teased, "She brought Little Bill wid her too." Grandpa had been a slave who ran away from Mississippi. His first name was Knight, and he had an air of importance. He had bought enough land that a lot of our family lived on his place. Aunt Butch's house was nearby, and Uncle Henry's, with two sets of twins, was just across the branch.

Before I went any further I knew I had to kiss Grandpa. My brother, Sweet, hated to come for that reason. Grandpa chewed tobacco, had a beard, and kissing him was messy. If you tried to slip past him, he would peck you on the head with his cane. I surrendered a quick kiss to him and ran in to the house.

Grandma was frail and going blind and had always lived in Texas. I got real close to her and she patted me on the head, but having

Mama there was the medicine she needed. So I went to my favorite place, the kitchen. I loved Grandma's kitchen—its long table with benches on each side. The kitchen was a log cabin attached to the front porch. Even though I didn't like Br'er Rabbit syrup, I wasn't about to refuse Aunt Butch's biscuits and some syrup at Grandma's. Grandma's house seemed nearer heaven. We were sharecroppers, but Grandpa owned all the land and as far as my eyes could see.

I didn't know where to go first. I could go by the chalk mine, stop by the well for a cool drink of water, or head down the bottom where the pecan trees grew. Grandpa's eyes twinkled as I took off.

Mama ran out the door yelling, "You be careful!"

But I was long gone.

Together in the Room

Together in the room
We wondered about each other
At 9:00 a.m.

Together in the room
Asian, African, Caucasian
Male, female, gay, straight, and bi.

Together in the room
Hoped for each other,
Friends, spouses, lovers, pairs, trios, individuals.

Together in the room
Giving the number
Of sex partners had in the last 12 months.

Twenty-four plus.
Sixty minutes later with
HIV tested arm around my date...

Together in the room.
Number
Twenty-five!

If You Believe
(The Whole Thang in a Nutshell)

For all ya'll
Who believe
Black folks
Ain't shit,
And you know who you are.

You're right.
Black folks
Ain't shit.

You are!

Si Tú Crees
(Todo en Una Cascara de Nuez)

Para todos los
Que creen que
Gente de color
No son mierda,
Y ustedes saben quienes son.

Dicen bien.
Gente de color
No son mierda.

Ustedes son!

Notes on Contributors

SALEEM ABDAL-KHAALIQ is a Los Angeles poet and freelance writer. He works as a job developer with Pasadena City College.

ÆTHRIDGE (ETHRIDGE SMITH) is a native New Yorker currently living in Los Angeles. His work has appeared in *ONTHEBUS*, *Spillway*, and *Insomnia*. He has published one book of poems, *Intimations*, and two chapbooks.

SUNJI ALI (GENE WILLIAMS), a poet and a retired educator and historian, has been published in *76th and San Pedro*, an IBWA anthology, and *Black Men Still Singing*, an anthology from Guild, Press Minnesota. He is founder and president of Soulvisions Productions, a traveling jazz, blues, rap and poetry performance group appearing weekly at various night spots and restaurants in the greater Los Angeles area.

CASSANDRA R. BAKER is currently the director of public relations for the ITC graduate school of theology in Atlanta, Georgia.

DONALD BAKEER is the author of the novel *Crips* and co-writer of the screenplay, *South Central*. Over the past 24 years, Bakeer has taught English in secondary schools in South Central L.A. As a 15-year member and former president of IBWA/LA, Bakeer edited IBWA's 1986 anthology, *76th and San Pedro*. He has also compiled three student poetry anthologies. His own book of poetry and short stories, *JOMO*, was published in 1971. Bakeer's new novel, *Inhale: Gasoline and Gunsmoke* (a story of the South Central L.A. uprising), was released summer 1994.

GEANORA BONNER is a native of Compton, California. She is currently a fifth grade teacher in Los Angeles and making progress on a novel.

GWEN BOOKER is a single parent who writes from Akron, Ohio. She reads for the blind, serves on the Speakers Bureau for the Akron Public Main Library, and serves with the Youth Motivation Task Force with the Private Industry Council. Recently, Gwen received a Woman of Distinction Award from the Western Reserve Girl Scout Council.

LELA BRANCH, born in 1932 in the rural Mississippi Delta and a graduate of California State University, currently resides in Warner Springs, California.

ERIC BROWN is an English major at James Madison University in Harrisonburg, Virginia. His poetry draws inspiration from the people of his childhood.

MALAIKA BROWN is a reporter for the *Los Angeles Sentinel.* She lives with her husband, Anthony, in Long Beach. "Holy Wars" is her first published fiction.

SHARONDA CALDWELL is a 24-year-old disabled student majoring in Recreation Therapy/Human Service at Cypress College.

GEORGE CLABON, a native of St. Louis, Missouri, migrated to Minnesota to attend Carleton College in Northfield. He currently resides in Minneapolis.

CECILIA CLINKSCALE is a poet, filmmaker, director, and writer living in Philadelphia, Pennsylvania. In November 1993, she received the National Library of Poetry Editors Choice Award. She has a B.A. in Communications and expects to complete her M.A. in African-American Studies this year, both from Temple University.

DENNIS CUTTEN is an active member of IBWA's Oakland, California branch. His work has appeared in *Beyond Baroque, Balance, Poetry Break,* and other publications.

ANN MARIE DAVIS is a native of Oakland, California. She has an art degree from California State University, Hayward.

ERIC JEROME DICKEY resides in Los Angeles County. He is currently shopping three contemporary African-American novels, *Hello, Cheaters: Caught Up in the Game,* and *black or white: and all that that implies,* as well as two screenplays, *Cappuccino* and *Letting Go.*

KHADIJAH FARABI-NANCE is an artist, story poet, storyteller, and fabric artist.

BYRON JOHN FITZGERALD writes from Los Angeles, California. His poetry has been published in *Our Twentieth Century's Greatest Poems* (1982) and *American Poetry Anthology,* Vol. VII #4 (1987). Fitzgerald earned B.A. (English) and M.A. (Ed. Administration) degrees from California State University, Los Angeles. He has been a teacher with the Los Angeles Unified School District for over twenty years.

RODNEY FOSTER is a Trinidadian-American currently residing in Pico Rivera, California. He immigrated to the U.S. in 1973 and attended Brooklyn College, majoring in psychology and education. He has self-published two books: *Remember Wen!* (1990) and *Walk In My Shoes* (1993).

VANESSA ORR FRANCIS is a graduate of California State University, Long Beach. She is the author of *The Blue Wanderer*, a self-published book of poetry, and is Advertising Standards Associate at Modern Maturity magazine.

MARIA S. FRENCH, PH.D., was born in Nicaragua, but grew up in Los Angeles. Her poetry has been exhibited in San Francisco. Recently, she has produced theater for high school students. Currently, she teaches at Widney High School in Los Angeles.

LILY GILL won first prize in the Los Angeles Pierce Writers Conference Short Story Fiction Contest. She is working on a novel-in-stories collection, and her stories have appeared in half a dozen publications.

ELIMU GOSS is an actor, dancer, and performance poet based in Los Angeles. Goss recently appeared in Sunji Ali's *Sweet Water Blues* at the Theater of Arts in Los Angeles.

PHYLLIS HARGROVE is an urban planner who lives in the Los Angeles area with her husband and daughter. She is a graduate of California State University, Long Beach.

SHIRLEY ANN HARRIS is the Director of Staff Development for the Watts Health Foundation, Inc. "The Day the Tears Stopped" is her first published short story.

HAZEL CLAYTON HARRISON is a past president of IBWA, Los Angeles. She received her B.S. and M.Ed. from Kent State University. Her poetry and prose have appeared in *Essence, American Visions*, the *Los Angeles Times*, and numerous journals and anthologies. She is the author of a collection of poetry and prose, *Winter in L.A.*

KEITH JAMES is a writer currently living in Amsterdam, The Netherlands. Soon, he will chronicle his travels to Denmark, Hungary, Belgium and, of course, The Netherlands for an American magazine.

ROSE WARREN KIRBY is currently a school librarian at Horace Mann Middle School in Los Angeles and a part-time English instructor at Los Angeles Southwest College. She received her B.A. and M.A. in English from North Texas University, and her Library Science Degree from California State University, Los Angeles. Her poetry reflects her life as a mother, grandmother, teacher, and deeply spiritual woman, striving to understand, interpret, and cope with her world.

KHEVEN LEE LAGRONE writes from Oakland, California. He is "...a man who has chosen his mind—not his penis or anger—as the tool of choice."

REGINA LYNCH-HUDSON has carved her niche in Atlanta's arts/entertainment industry writing media kits, press releases, radio jingles, and maga zine/newspaper articles.

CHARLES MCGILL, a past president of IBWA/LA, passed away on September 2, 1993 at the age of 51. Under the name of Cheo, the Metro Poet, McGill wrote, performed, and published many works in Rochester, New York; Washington, D.C.; and Los Angeles, California.

RICHARD MOORE is president of IBWA Local 5 in Oakland. He is the author of *The Empire Strikes Black*, *Sexutopia*, and other books.

JEMELA MWELU is a Los Angeles actor, poet, singer, producer, and playwright. Her poetry has appeared in *Blind Alleys*, *Moreno* magazine, and *Swords Into Ploughshares* (anthology).

RITA MYLES is a registered nurse and member of IBWA. She resides in Los Angeles.

RUBI OLIVER-WHITESIDE is a freelance writer living in San Francisco. Currently, she is working on a fictional historical trilogy about the resistance of African Queen Nzinga and free African American women, slave trade, and slavery in the U.S.

RICARDA M. PAYNE is a poet currently living in Miami, Florida. She is a native Southern Californian and a graduate of Howard University.

DORIS K. REED writes from Los Angeles. Her work has been published in *Essence*, *Science of Mind* magazine, the *Los Angeles Sentinel*, the *Los Angeles Times*, and numerous anthologies.

EL RIVERA was born in Harlem in 1959, orphaned at age 11, reared as a ward of the state of Maryland, and currently resides in Los Angeles.

RANDY ROSS, PH.D., writes from Huntington Park, California, that "Red's Rhythm" is part of a collection of stories he is developing that explores the plight and promise of being a Black man in America. This collection includes a prize-winning story in *Ebony's* Gertrude Johnson Williams literary contest as well as stories that have been or will be published in *Maryland Review* and *African American Review*.

BEVERLY RUSSELL is a poet and writer from Toluca Lake, California. Her work has been published in several magazines and anthologies.

ANNE RUTLEDGE is a retired educator (associate professor of history and political science at Alabama A&M University), writer, and poet. Two of her books have been published: *Soul on Fire* (1967) and *Double the Pleasure* (1988). Her poetry has been published in several publications.

CHERENE MONIQUE SHERRARD is currently an English/American Studies major at UCLA. She plans to become a professor and professional writer.

MARK SIMMONS is a 28-year-old black gay writer living in Los Angeles. His poetry and short stories have appeared in *Kuumba, Other Countries Journal, Spectrum, The James White Review*, and *Ecce Queer*. Also, his journalistic essays have appeared in numerous publications.

SIDNEY SINGLETON is a Los Angeles performance poet. He has been affiliated with IBWA since 1986. He is currently a member of Comfort, Edify and Exhort (C.E.E.), a poetry and song ministry group.

NATASHA TARPLEY graduated with honors from Harvard University in 1993, receiving her B.A. in African American Studies. She is currently attending Georgetown University Law Center. She is the editor of *Testimony*, an anthology of writings by Black College Students (Beacon Press, 1994). Her work has appeared in *Essence, Callaloo, African American Review, Obsidian II*, among others. She is the recipient of a 1994 fellowship for poetry from the National Endowment for the Arts.

ALI MAXWELL TAYLOR currently teaches English, speech, and drama in Granada Hills, CA. She has B.A. and M.A. degrees and is currently pursuing a doctorate at Pepperdine University. Taylor has written and directed many school programs and plays and has been involved in community theatre as writer/director/actress. She was a 1991 semifinalist for the California Teacher of the Year honor.

SYBIL VAUGHN is an Atlanta poet, essayist, thinker, columnist, and editor of the *Cut-Up*. Her work has appeared in the *Atlanta Constitution* and Boston's *Urban Beat*.

MIKA WEBB is a 19 year old college student who attends Spelman College. Her work has been published in *YSB* magazine, *Voices of Black Strength* (anthology) and Spellman College's newspaper, *Spotlight*.

BETTY WELCH grew up in South Los Angeles. She holds a B.A. in journalism from the University of La Verne.

STEPHANIE M. WHITNEY holds a B.A. in English from UCLA and teaches full-time with the Los Angeles Unified School District. "Go Life" is her first published poem.

NIAMA LESLIE JOANN WILLIAMS, a native of Los Angeles, is a doctoral student and teaching assistant within the African American Studies department of Temple University located in Philadelphia, Pennsylvania.

JESSIE DAWSON WILSON is the author of *Yeller Gal: Memoir of a Sharecropper's Daughter*, which she wrote while attending USC's Master of Professional Writing Program. The book won the 1992 Associated Writing Program's Intro Award for nonfiction, an excerpt was published in the *Black Warrior Review* and it has been adapted to a screen play. Currently, Jessie is an adjunct faculty member of the Union Institute where she teaches Creative Writing and Business Technical Writing.

C. JEROME WOODS is a writer and community activist who currently resides in the West Adams district of Los Angeles. He is the author of two chapbooks: *Love Songs & Heartbreaks* and *Self Portrait*.

Spirits of the Waters

Patrons who contributed financial aid and services in support of this publication are listed below in three categories. Through their kindness, our "river crossings" was made lighter, more reverent, and in celebration!

INDIVIDUALS

DORIS AARONS
JACQUELINE ALEXANDER
STEPHANIE ANDERSON
JAN ARMSTRONG
STEPHANIE AUSTIN
PAMELA BAKER
DERRICK BRICE
MARTIN CADRES
ADALBERTO CARAVALHO
WENDELL CARMICHAEL
EDNA CRUTCHFIELD
MARIA S. FRENCH
EDWINA GAINES
RAMONA GOINS
MR. & MRS. WENDELL GREER, JR.
TERRY & HAZEL HARRISON
DAVID & JENNIFER HAWES-DAWSON
EARNEST JACKSON
ROBERT E. JEFFERSON
MARC L. KELLY
MS. NOMA LEMOINE
MARIVALDO S. NERY
JAY NOLAN
JIM PERKINS
MRS. JESSE J. PETERS

Ms. Brenonda Poulson
Charles A. Proctor III
Ms. Kim Ramsey
Randy & Juana Ross
Bernie & Ninfa Rubalcava
Mrs Jane Saca
Billie Atkins Sanders
Paula Santos
Arlance D. Sims
Suzanne M. Stewart
Ernest E. Stroman
Seth & Serge Tanner
Christopher Vaughn
James L. Wheaton
Marsha Wiederhorn
William Terrence Wright

ORGANIZATIONS

The Friends Of William Grant Still
2520 West View Street, Los Angeles, California 90016
(213) 734-1164

Widney High School Athletic Fund
Board of Directors: Les Hayes, Pat Ninke, Leroy Ransom, Marty Todd
Teams: **L.A. Kodiaks, So. Calif. Sunrise, L.A. Stars**

BUSINESSES

The Black Inventions Museum—Sala Enterprises
P.O. Box 76122
Los Angeles, California 90076

Clark & Associates
1387 West 29th Street, Los Angeles, California 90007
(213) 766-8696

Culture Videos
1239 South Harvard Boulevard, Los Angeles, California 90006
(213) 735-6867

About the Editor

C Jerome Woods holds a Master's Degree in Education from California State University at Los Angeles and is the author of two poetry chapbooks: *Love Songs & Heartbreaks* and *Self Portrait*.

He is currently a member of the First A.M.E. Church Drama Department, board member for St. Elmo Village (an arts institution in L.A.), Friends of William Grant Still Arts Center, and International Black Writers & Artists, Los Angeles. In addition, he has done Public Relations for the California Association for Health, Physical Education, Recreation and Dance, and was co-program book editor for the 1992 International Black Dance Companies Conference.

He is a Creative Consultant and Education Specialist living in Los Angeles, California.